Contents

Introduction

In his novel *Hard Times* Charles Dickens created a character named Mr. Gradgrind, who presided over The School of Hard Facts. During one class session, Mr. Gradgrind called on a student for the definition of a horse.

Well-schooled, the little Gradgrind recited: "Quadruped. Gramnivorous. Forty teeth, namely twenty-four grinders, four eyeteeth, and twelve incisive. Sheds coat in the spring; in marshy countries sheds hoofs too. Hoofs hard, but requiring to be shod with iron. Age known by marks in mouth." And so on.

At the risk of sounding like Mr. Gradgrind, we present you with this book of questions, the answers to which require a knowledge of Hard Facts. But they require a few other elements too: broad and deep reading, the ability to make imaginative leaps, a gift for educated guessing, and a playful nature. Playing the literary games included here will do one of two things: (a) reinforce your sense of superiority and smugness, because you know the answers to most of the questions; or (b) remind you of (or introduce you to) some wonderful moments in the lives of people who have lived in the imaginations of readers for hundreds of years.

For people, not Hard Facts, are what literature is all about. And life, not trivia, is the energizing force of great writing. When I was invited to write this book about literary trivia, I at first recoiled. Trivia! Insignificant or inessential matters? Is that what my life of living, breathing, teaching, writing literature boiled down to? How depressing.

Then, I got beyond the first (Gradgrindian) definition of trivia, and found this dictionary note: "From the Latin, *trivium*, 'the place where three roads meet; the public square.' " Aha! This is the exact forum that I—as writer, scholar, teacher, and lover of literature—have been looking for all along! In this book itself you'll find the intersection of Grub Street (where people have historically written in plain language for people on the run) and Academe (where people with specialized knowledge increase and preserve that knowledge and pass it along). So, *trivium*, a meeting place. I hope you enjoy meeting here as much as I do.

In this, our World of Literature, you'll test your knowledge on everything from Bible stories to newspaper columnists. The selection of materials is heavy on Literature of the Western World, and that originally written in English, Greek, or Latin. But you will find the stray reference to other literary cultures as well.

The questions here are highly idiosyncratic. I've included literature that I know well and love. Another writer would have included other selections. If your favorite works are overlooked, let us know; perhaps there'll be a Son (or Daughter) of Whiz Quiz.

We tried to choose questions that would stretch you, along with those that are fairly basic. There is a trick question or two, and I think you'll find some surprises—especially in Chapter 9, where Copy Cats confess to borrowing material from one another.

Borrowing and lending, and passing information back and forth and down the halls of time, are legitimate acts; in fact, they keep literature alive for each new generation, and each generation enriches the legacy with its own additions and interpretations. The ability to imagine richly and write well is a gift. Like all gifts, it is meant to be shared, and the only illegitimate use of our World of Literature is hoarding it, claiming it for ourselves alone, and refusing to pass it on or give it away.

These gifts we have in stories, novels, poetry, plays, and imaginative nonfiction come to us because writers and artists like to play. Making a stunning poem is very hard. But it is also a game. Poets make the game hard for the fun of it, so they can solve the problems they set for themselves. And they make the hard look easy. That's also a part of the game. The German critic Baumgarten spoke of the central impulse toward poetry, as toward art, as *Spieltrieb*, the play impulse.

So play away. That's what this book is for. Play the games here with yourself, your partner, your family, or have a group of friends in to test themselves. Some of the questions are tough (my son, Tim, calls this book "Jeopardy for Geniuses"), and some will make you feel terribly bright. (Of course, you are, or you wouldn't be reading this book to start with!)

Besides expressing my thanks to my editors for making a book out of a disparate collection of Q's and A's, I want to thank a few other literature lovers for passing that gift on to me: my mother, the poet Margaret Ellen Slack, who, from the time I could read and raise Q's made me look up the A's for myself (then she would help me interpret); my graduate school friend and fellow lover of all things literate, attorney Barbara Standal; and my husband, Jerry, Trivia King of the Universe.

This book, like Mr. Gradgrind's collection of innumerable Hard Facts, is only a beginning. It is meant to prepare you to enter, or re-enter, the magic world of great writing. So have fun. Enjoy the book with a friend or two. Then close it and run, don't walk, to your nearest library for another handful of riches from the World of Literature.

Miracles and Lamentations: The Bible as Literature

The Bible contains almost every literary genre. For example, it gives us songs—those of Solomon, Deborah, Lamech, and Miriam. It contains folk tales, legends, romances, tragedies, short stories. It even contains a novel—the ironic story of Esther. The Bible contains poetry—love lyrics, odes, hymns, dramatic monologues, the puzzling and touching story of Job, the exalted poetry of the prophets. It contains wildly surrealistic drama in Revelations, and it teases us with its riddles, fables, and, above all, its thoughtful parables. It tells us of crooked kings, mad men, fallen women, lost children, heroic people of all races. It talks of cities that tumble down at the sound of trumpets, seas that part, and a disobedient woman who turns into a pillar of salt.

The Bible has shaped the lives of men and women for more than two millennia. It is the work most frequently referred to in the English language.

To test your knowledge of the Bible, let's start with some questions on the more familiar stories.

❶ What does the Bible say of God's activities prior to Creation?

❷ Who told the first lie in the Bible?

❸ God told Adam and Eve not to eat from a certain tree. But they disobeyed Him. Which tree was that?

❹ Why did Adam and Eve dress themselves in leaves?

❺ God punished the first couple by sending them out of the Garden of Eden. At what gate did God place an angel with a sword to see that they got out and stayed out?

6 Why did Cain, Adam and Eve's firstborn, kill his brother, Abel?

7 Was it Cain or Abel who said to God, "Am I my brother's keeper?"

8 How did God punish Cain for his crime?

9 How many human generations occurred between Adam and Eve and the flood?

10 How many years did God give Noah to complete the ark?

11 Here's a Biblical math problem: Noah was only three score years old when it began to rain. This was 369 years younger than Methusalah was when the older man died. How old were both Noah and Methusalah?

12 How long did Noah and his crew remain in the ark?

13 On what mountain did Noah's ark finally come to rest?

14 What object did God put in the sky as a promise to Noah that he would never again destroy the world by flood?

15 According to Genesis, when the descendants of Noah began to build a tower up to Heaven, what did God do to stop them?

16 With whom did God make a covenant, telling him that he would be father of a host of nations?

17 For this two-parter, do you know: (a) who was the mother of Abraham's son Isaac, and (b) how old Abraham was when Isaac was born?

18 What test did God put to Abraham that involved his son Isaac?

19 What two cities did God destroy because the men there were so corrupt?

20 When Lot and his family fled the wicked city that God was about to destroy, God warned them not to look back as they ran. But Lot's wife disobeyed. What happened to her?

21 Lot's two daughters lived with him in a cave after they fled the wicked city. One daughter bore a son called Moab; the other a son called Ben-ammi. Who was the father of these boys?

22 Abraham's son Isaac had twin sons. For this three-parter: (a) what are their names, (b) which one traded his birthright for "a mess of pottage," and (c) which one became the father of the children of Israel?

23 Joseph had a coat of many colors given to him by his father. This made his brothers jealous, and they plotted to kill him. But one brother refused to go along, and the plan was changed. What was this brother's name?

24 How many tribes of Israel were there?

25 Why was the baby Moses, born in Egypt, put in a basket made of bulrushes and placed beside a river?

26 Who found Moses?

27 Ironically, who became Moses' nursemaid?

28 When Moses grew into a man, God addressed him in a peculiar fashion and told him that he would save the children of Israel. How did God speak to Moses?

29 To whom did Moses say, "Let my people go"?

30 Why did Moses bring ten plagues, including frogs, maggots, flies, boils, and pestilence on Egypt?

31 Moses' brother Aaron accompanied Moses as he led the children of Israel. What special magical item did Aaron have that convinced the Israelites to follow them?

32 How long did God decree that the Israelites wander in the wilderness?

33 What food did God send the Israelites as they wandered in the desert?

34 For a three-part question: (a) on what mountain did God give Moses the Ten Commandments, (b) what were the Commandments written on, and (c) how long did Moses remain on the mountain?

35 What did Aaron do to appease the impatient Israelites who were waiting for Moses to come down from the mountain?

36 What two structures did God ask Moses to make for Him?

37 Did Moses see the Promised Land?

38 Who followed Moses as leader of the children of Israel?

39 In the Book of Esther, this king made Queen Vashti step down as queen, to be replaced by Esther. What was his name?

40 To whom did Esther send the message, "And if I perish, I perish"?

41 For whose hanging did Haman set up a gallows seventy-five feet high? Who actually met his death on these gallows?

Here are some Old Testament characters you should be able to identify by a single trait or event in their lives.

42 Let's begin with this one: Who found himself in the belly of a great fish?

43 Whose strength was dependent on his long hair? For extra credit, who found out his secret and caused his downfall?

44 Which king of Israel was known for his wisdom?

45 Which Biblical character was known for his patience?

46 Who dreamed of a ladder to Heaven?

47 Who made the walls of Jericho come tumbling down?

48 What Biblical character was so devoted to her mother-in-law that she said: "For whither thou goest, I will go; and where thou lodgest, I will lodge: thy people shall be my people, and thy God my God"?

49 Because King David wanted this man's wife, the king sent him to the front of the battle lines, knowing he would be killed. Who was the man, and who was his wife?

50 What Biblical character was left hanging by his hair from the branches of an oak tree?

51 Here's a three-parter: (a) how many Hebrews were thrown into the fiery furnace, (b) can you name them, and (c) why were they thrown into the fire?

52 Who killed a huge creature with a flying rock?

53 What Babylonian king had dreams that he asked Daniel to interpret?

54 At whose feast was Daniel asked to interpret the writing on the wall?

55 What queen was thrown out of a window, but nothing of her was found except her skull, her feet, and the palms of her hands?

56 The Book of Judges tells the story of the first woman judge. This judge agreed to accompany Barak and ten thousand men into battle, but warned that if she went, the commander of forces, Sisera, would "fall into the hands of a woman." The prophecy of this judge proved correct. What was the name of (a) the judge, and (b) who was the woman into whose hands Sisera fell?

57 Let's try a Matching Question. Can you match the wives on the left with

their husbands on the right? (There is one less husband than wife. For extra credit, can you say why?)

Wife	Husband
1. Ruth	**(a)** Aquila
2. Rebecca	**(b)** Uriah
3. Gomer	**(c)** Boaz
4. Zipporah	**(d)** Hosea
5. Susanna	**(e)** Moses
6. Bathsheba	**(f)** Shechem
7. Priscilla	**(g)** Isaac
8. Leah	**(h)** Joakim
9. Dinah	**(i)** Ananias
10. Sapphira	**(j)** Jacob
11. Rachel	

58 Who wrote the most songs in the Bible?

59 What Biblical character had 700 wives and 300 concubines?

60 What wealthy widow of Judah cut off the head of Nebuchadnezzar's general, Holofernes?

61 Who was thrown into the lion's den as punishment, and for what was he being punished?

62 Let's see how much you know about the Old Testament prophets. Try matching the prophets in the column at the left with the descriptions in the column at the right.

Prophet	Description
1. Isaiah	**(a)** He saw wheels of fire and fiery clouds filled with four living creatures.
2. Jeremiah	**(b)** He was swept away in a whirlwind.
3. Ezekial	**(c)** Known for his angry lamentations; Baruch was his amanuensis.
4. Elijah	**(d)** He foretold that Jesus would be born in Bethlehem.
5. Micah	**(e)** God appointed him as watchman for the Israelites.

63 What was the name of the group—rivals of the people of Israel—that has become a derogatory term denoting uncultured materialism?

64 According to Moses, who was the false god, the "loathsome god of the Ammonites"?

Let's move on to the New Testament and see how well you do with questions concerning Jesus, his family, his teachings, and the apostles.

65 From what direction did the three Wise Men come?

66 What three gifts did the Wise Men bring to the infant Jesus?

67 What two Greek words—the first and last letters of the Greek alphabet—did Jesus use in describing himself as the "beginning" and the "end"?

68 Where did Mary, Joseph, and Jesus live?

69 After the birth of Jesus, where did the three flee to escape Herod's plan to kill male children?

70 Who was stoned to death for preaching about Jesus?

71 Name the angel who spoke to Mary and told her she would conceive and bear a child.

72 How many apostles did Jesus recruit? For extra credit, can you name them?

73 Thought by some scholars to be the second most important figure in Christianity after Jesus, this apostle's name was once Saul. By what name is he better known?

74 Simon—"the rock"—is the most prominent of all the apostles. Jesus

chose to build His church on him. But what name is he better known?

75 In what garden was Jesus arrested?

76 Here's a three-parter: (a) with what loving gesture did an apostle betray Jesus, (b) for how much money was Christ betrayed, and (c) what was the name of the betrayer?

77 At what meal did Jesus prepare his apostles to live without him and make a bond between himself and the future Christian community?

78 Although he later claimed to be "innocent of the blood of this person," who ordered the crucifixion of Christ?

79 What was placed on the head of Christ as he carried the cross?

80 For how many hours did Jesus hang on the cross?

81 Here's a two-parter: (a) what event happened at Golgotha, and (b) what is another name for Golgotha?

82 Name the writers of the four Gospels of the New Testament.

83 Which of the Gospel writers was a physician?

84 According to the Gospel of Matthew, Jesus fed 5,000 men—plus women and children—with how many loaves and how many fishes?

85 Who, besides Jesus, walked on water?

86 How many brothers and sisters did Jesus have?

87 According to the Gospel of Matthew, it is easier for a camel to go through the eye of a needle than for whom to enter the Kingdom of Heaven?

88 When Satan fell from Heaven, who saw him fall?

89 In the parable of the ten virgins, how many were wise and how many foolish?

90 Who asked God this question: "Eli, Eli, Lama sabachthani?"

91 What is the term for the event, mentioned in Revelations, when the Son of God will come again to earth?

92 What is the name of the great battlefield where, at the end of the world, the powers of good and evil will fight to the finish?

93 In the Old Testament, Ezekial, Daniel, Joel, Zechariah, and others are

called apocalyptic prophets, meaning they foresee the end of the world. What book in the New Testament is best known for being apocalyptic, and who wrote it?

94 The Bible mentions a scroll that was closed with Seven Seals. When the first four seals were opened, four horses and their riders emerged. Can you: (a) name the colors of the four horses and their riders, and (b) tell what the riders were called?

95 Both Luke and Matthew mention what has come to be known as the Golden Rule. Can you recite it?

96 How many years did Jesus live?

97 What is the name of the man whom Jesus raised from the dead?

98 Joseph, husband of Mary, was not simply a humble carpenter as many think. From whom was he descended?

99 What rhetorical method did Jesus typically use to teach his followers?

100 In one of Jesus's most famous stories, a young man took his share of his inheritance and wasted it. His father was saddened and finally gave him up for dead, but when the boy returned home, the father made a great feast for

him and killed the best fatted calf. By what name do we know the young man?

101 What is Jesus's most quoted sermon?

102 What was the term for the most skeptical apostle?

103 What are the Beatitudes, and with what word does each Beatitude begin?

104 What Biblical character was known for her exquisitely layered filmy costume and her ability to dance?

Here are some short quotations from the Bible. See how many you can finish.

105 "For whatsoever a man soweth that shall he ________."

106 "Greater love hath no man than this, that ________."

107 "For what shall it profit a man, if he shall gain all the world and lose ________."

108 "What doth the Lord require of thee, but to do justly and to love mercy, and to ________."

109 "A time to love, and time to hate; a time of war, and ________."

110 "A man hath no better thing under the sun, than to eat, and to ______."

111 "Vanity of vanities; all is ________."

112 "There is nothing new ________."

Here are some fairly tough questions about the history of the Bible as a book and how it has come down to us. See how well you do on them.

113 What version of the Bible do most people read?

114 The first five books of the Bible are sometimes called "The Books of Moses." They are also referred to as: (a) the Apocrypha, (b) the Pentateuch, or (c) the Decalogues?

115 Can you name the first five books of the Bible?

116 Who translated both Old and New Testaments from the Latin Vulgate of Saint Jerome into the English of his day?

117 This man is sometimes called the Father of the English Bible. He was the first to print the New Testament (in the city of Worms in 1526) in English; he was attempting to translate the Old Testament into English and had finished the first five books, when he was

captured, convicted of heresy, and burned at the stake. Who was he?

118 Which is longer, the Old Testament or the New Testament?

119 What group of people were, by an Act of Parliament of 1543, forbidden to read the Bible publicly or privately under pain of imprisonment?

120 How many books are in the Old Testament? How many are in the New Testament?

121 In what language was the Old Testament written? What about the New Testament?

122 Here's a final two-parter: The Dead Sea Scrolls, documents illuminating the evolution of Judaism and the origin of Christianity, were discovered in 1947. (a) In what country were they found, and (b) in what strange location in that country?

123 In what book do the Bride and Bridegroom recite love lyrics to one another?

124 What is the one book in the Bible in which the word "God" does not appear?

Answers

① *Nothing. The Bible begins: "In the beginning God created the heavens and the earth." (Genesis 1:1)*

② *The serpent. Speaking to Eve, he said, "Ye shall not surely die." (Genesis 3:4)*

③ *They ate from the Tree of the Knowledge of Good and Evil. (Genesis 2:16)*

④ *To cover their nakedness because they were ashamed. (Genesis 3:7)*

⑤ *At the gate east of Eden. (Genesis 3:24)*

⑥ *Cain slew Abel because he was jealous of him. Both Cain and Abel had made offerings to God; Abel's offering pleased God, but Cain's did not. This made Cain jealous. (Genesis 4:4-16)*

⑦ *After denying he knew the whereabouts of Abel, Cain asked God, "Am I my brother's keeper?" (Genesis 4:4-16)*

⑧ *God condemned Cain to a life of wandering in a distant land, the land of Nod, east of Eden. (Genesis 4:12-16)*

⑨ *Ten human generations occurred between the two. (Genesis 5:1-32)*

⑩ *God gave Noah 120 years to build the ark. (Genesis 6:9-17)*

⑪ *Noah was 600 years old and Methusalah was 969. (Genesis 5:27 and 7:11-12)*

⑫ *Noah remained in the ark one year and seventeen days. (Genesis 8:1-5)*

⑬ *The ark rested on Mount Ararat. (Genesis 8:4-5)*

⑭ *God put a rainbow in the sky as a promise that he would never again destroy the world by flood. (A verse by the novelist James Baldwin puts it this way: "God gave Noah the rainbow sign, No more water, the fire next time.") (Genesis 9:13-14)*

⑮ *God made them speak in different tongues and dispersed them throughout the world. The name of the tower was Babel, from which we get the word "babble." (Genesis 11:1-2)*

⑯ *God made this covenant with Abraham. (Genesis 17:2-5)*

⑰ *(a) Sarah was the mother of Isaac. (b) In their later years—Abraham was one-hundred years old when Isaac was born and Sarah was ninety-nine—God blessed them with a child. (Genesis 21: 1-13)*

⑱ *God told Abraham to take Isaac off to a hill and sacrifice him. Abraham obeyed, even to binding the boy and laying him on firewood for the sacrifice, but as Abraham lifted his knife to slay his son, an angel appeared and stopped him. Recognizing Abraham as a God-fearing man, God sent a ram to be sacrificed in place of Isaac. (Genesis 22:1-19)*

⑲ *Sodom and Gomorrah. God planned to destroy the two cities and their inhabitants, but Abraham convinced God to let the good men escape and destroy only those who displeased Him. (Genesis 18 and 19)*

⑳ *Lot's wife was turned into a pillar of salt when she turned back to look as God rained down fire and brimstone on the city of Sodom. (Genesis 19:26-27)*

㉑ *Lot was the father of his daughters' sons. The isolated daughters despaired of meeting men and having children, so they made Lot drunk and seduced him "to keep the family alive" through their father. (Genesis 25:15-28)*

㉒ *(a) Jacob and Esau. (b) Esau, Isaac's eldest son, should have inherited the covenant with God that Abraham passed on to Isaac. But when he was sick and hungry, Esau traded his birthright to Jacob for food, "a mess of pottage." (c) Jacob became the father of the Israelites. (Genesis 25:24-26)*

㉓ *Reuben, Joseph's eldest brother, refused to kill him. (Genesis 37:1-37)*

(24) There were twelve tribes of Israel. Jacob had twelve sons and each fathered a tribe of Israel. The twelve tribes as represented by pieces of Canaanite territory are: Reuben, Simeon, Judah, Dan, Gad, Issacher, Zebulun, Asher, Nephtali, Benjamin, Ephraim, and Manasseh.

(25) So Moses would not be killed. Pharaoh had directed that "Every son that is born to the Hebrews" be thrown into the Nile. (He had resolved to exterminate the Israelites.) (Exodus 1:22)

(26) Pharoah's daughter found Moses and sent for a nursemaid to help rear him. (Exodus 2:1-2)

(27) Moses's mother herself became his nursemaid. Moses's sister Miriam had hidden in the bushes beside the water and had seen Pharaoh's daughter take the baby from the river's edge. Miriam offered her mother as nursemaid for the baby. (Exodus 2:1-12)

(28) God spoke to Moses through an angel in a burning bush. (Exodus 5:1-4)

(29) Moses entreated Pharaoh with these words. (The Israelites had "groaned in slavery" to the Egyptians.) (Exodus 5:1-4)

(30) God caused ten plagues to befall the Egyptians as He urged Pharaoh to let

the Israelites go with Moses. The final plague was the overnight death of all animals and first-born Egyptian children. (Exodus 8-12)

㉛ *Aaron had a magical rod with which he could perform miracles. (Exodus 7:8)*

㉜ *Forty years.*

㉝ *Manna, "the bread which the Lord has given you [the Israelites] to eat." (Exodus 16:14-15). Manna was not actually bread, but a sweet, sticky substance produced by insects that suck the tender twigs of tamarisk bushes in the desert region. This "honeydew excretion" falls to the ground and solidifies. The solid residue can then be gathered and used for food.*

㉞ *(a) Mount Sinai, (b) stone tablets, and (c) forty days and forty nights. (Exodus 19:24 and 24:18)*

㉟ *When the Israelites became restless waiting for Moses, Aaron took golden earrings and other ornaments from the people and fashioned a golden god in the shape of a calf. (Exodus 32:2-4)*

㊱ *A Tabernacle (tent where Moses could "speak" with God) and the Ark of the Covenant (a chest or box in which Moses placed the two stone tablets inscribed with the Ten Commandments). (Exodus 25:10 and 25:12)*

(37) *Yes, Moses saw the Promised Land from the top of Pisgah on Mount Nebo, but he did not enter the Promised Land. He died before the Israelites crossed over the Jordan River. (Deuteronomy 34)*

(38) *Joshua took Moses's place as leader. (Joshua 1:1-5)*

(39) *King Ahasuerus.*

(40) *To Mordecai. Haman, the grand vizier, convinced King Ahasuerus to decree that all Jews be put to death. Mordecai sent the information to Esther, and she, from inside the king's palace, sent back the message that she would intercede for her people, even if she perished. (Esther 4)*

(41) *Haman set up the gallows to hang Mordecai, Esther's cousin, whom he attempted to put out of favor with the king. However, Haman himself was hanged on the gallows, giving an ironic end to the historical novel of Esther. (Esther 3, 4, 6-9)*

(42) *Jonah found himself inside a great fish. God had sent Jonah on a dangerous errand, and Jonah tried to avoid it by getting on a ship and running away. But his shipmates thought he brought bad luck, so they tossed him overboard, and he was swallowed by a big fish. After three days and three nights, the fish threw up his dinner on dry land. (Jonah)*

(43) *Samson's great strength was in his hair, which had never been cut. Delilah found out his secret and told it to Samson's enemy, the Philistines, who came and shaved his head while he slept. They put out Samson's eyes and put him in prison in Gaza to grind corn. But his hair began to grow in, and when the Philistines sent for him to mock him, he pulled down the pillars of the house, killing 3,000 Philistines. Unfortunately, he killed himself in the act as well. (Judges)*

(44) *King Solomon. God gave Solomon superior wisdom. When two women, both claiming to be the mother of the same child, came before him, he ordered that the baby be cut in two and that each woman take half of it. When one woman was appalled and refused, King Solomon proclaimed her the real mother. (I Kings; I Chronicles)*

(45) *Job. Job was a man who became the object of a wager between God and Satan. Satan bet God that Job could be made so miserable that he would curse God. Job's family, fortune, flocks, and herds were taken from him, and he was afflicted with boils. Still he did not curse God. A number of well-meaning friends tried to explain to Job why God treated him in this manner, but no satisfactory answer is reached in this puzzling Biblical story. Job simply suffers and he never understands why—though eventually God restores his fortune. (Job)*

(46) *Jacob, son of Isaac and Rebecca and twin of Esau, took a voyage to find a wife. One night he lay down to sleep using a stone for a pillow. He dreamed he saw a ladder set between Earth and Heaven and angels going up and down it. When he woke he made the stone into a pillar and poured oil over it, calling the place Bethel: the Lord's house. (Genesis 28:10)*

(47) *Joshua. In one of his many adventures in leading his people through the wilderness to the Promised Land, Joshua and his companions caused the walls of Jericho to come tumbling down after they circled the walls of the city thirteen times, blowing trumpets and shouting. (Joshua 6:1-21)*

(48) *Ruth was the devoted daughter-in-law who promised to go wherever Naomi, her mother-in-law, went. (Book of Ruth)*

(49) *David sent Uriah to the front lines, knowing he would be killed, because David wanted Bathsheba for his wife. David did marry Bathsheba, who later bore him a son, Solomon. (2 Samuel 11:2)*

(50) *Absalom. He was the third of King David's seventeen sons. He had a luxurious head of hair. He was a troublemaker, and led a rebellion against his father. While riding a mule, Absalom caught his hair in the branches of an oak tree and was left hanging when the mule walked on.*

Joab, an enemy, found him hanging in the tree and stabbed him. (2 Samuel 18:9-18)

(51) *(a) Three Hebrews were thrown into the fiery furnace. (b) Shadrach, Meshach, and Abed-nego were their names. (c) They refused to worship the golden image that King Nebuchadnezzar set up, so he threw them in the blazing furnace. But God walked with them in the furnace, and they were not singed. (Daniel 3:12-23)*

(52) *David. He was the seventh of the seven sons of Jesse, king of Judah. When he was a boy, the giant Goliath challenged to personal combat any Israelite brave enough to take him on. David had only five smooth stones and a sling, but he answered the challenge and struck Goliath in the forehead with the first stone. The blow killed him, and David cut off his head. (1 Samuel, 2 Samuel)*

(53) *King Nebuchadnezzar. (Daniel 2)*

(54) *Belshazzar's Feast. King Belshazzar gave a feast, and there a human hand appeared writing on the plaster of the palace wall. The words written were "mene mene tekel u-pharsin." Daniel was called to interpret the words, and he told the king that the message meant: God has numbered the days of your kingdom and brought it to an end; you have been weighed in the balance and found wanting; and your kingdom has been divided and given to the Medes and Persians. That*

night Belshazzar was killed and Darius took over the kingdom. (Daniel 5)

(55) *Jezebel, the wicked queen of Israel, who attempted to kill Elijah and other prophets. (2 Kings 9:30).*

(56) *Deborah was the judge, and Jael was the woman.*

(57) *There is one less man here because Jacob had two wives. (Genesis 29). 1(c) Ruth/Boas, 2(g) Rebecca/Isaac, 3(d) Gomer/Hosea, 4(e) Zipporah/Moses, 5(h) Susanna/Joakim, 6(b) Bathsheba/Uriah, 7(a) Priscilla/Aquila, 8(j) Leah/Jacob, 9(f) Dinah/Shechem, 10(i) Sapphira/Ananias, 11(j) Rachel/Jacob*

(58) *King David wrote most of the songs in the Bible. The Psalms (sometimes called the Psalms of David) are traditionally attributed to him, though he signed only seventy-three of the one hundred fifty.*

(59) *King Solomon had 700 wives and 300 concubines. (1 Kings 11:1-3)*

(60) *Judith (in the Apocrypha). King Nebuchadnezzar sent Holofernes, his commander-in-chief, to wipe out the Israelites. A beautiful widow, Judith, tricked him. She accompanied him to a banquet, urged him to drink too much, went back to his tent with him, and when he passed out, cut off his head and had it hung out for*

his troops to see. This act so frightened his men that the Israelites, vastly outnumbered, overcame them.

(61) *Daniel was thrown into the lion's den as punishment for praying to God. The next morning he was found unscathed and was released.*

(62) *1(e), 2(c), 3(a), 4(b), 5(d).*

(63) *Philistines.*

(64) *Moloch.*

(65) *The Wise Men came from the East. (The Gospels)*

(66) *The gifts the Wise Men brought to the baby Jesus were gold, frankincense and myrrh. (The Gospels)*

(67) *Jesus said, "I am the alpha and omega, the beginning and the end." (Revelations 1:8)*

(68) *The three lived in Nazareth. (Matthew 2:23)*

(69) *They fled to Egypt. (Matthew 2:1)*

(70) *Stephen. In the retelling of the story of Moses in the New Testament, the people of Israel had forgotten how they had been brought from Egypt and they had forsaken the Holy Spirit. Stephen, however, was filled with the Holy*

Spirit and cried out that he could see God and Jesus in a rift in the sky, and Man standing at God's right hand. The crowd rushed him and stoned him to death. Saul was witness to this and did not try to stop the murder. (Acts 7:51-60)

(71) *Gabriel was the angel that spoke to Mary. "Be thou not afraid," said the angel. "You shall conceive and bear a son and you shall give him the name Jesus." (Luke 1:26)*

(72) *There were twelve apostles. Jesus also picked seventy more disciples to help him further his teachings. The apostles were Peter, John, Judas, Thomas, James, Thaddaeus, Matthew, Bartholomew, Simon, Andrew, Philip, Titus. (The Gospels)*

(73) *Paul.*

(74) *Simon was called Peter. (Peter means "rock" in Greek.)*

(75) *He was arrested in the Garden of Gethsemane on the Mount of Olives. (Matthew 26:36)*

(76) *(a) Jesus was betrayed by a kiss. (b) He was betrayed for thirty pieces of silver. (c) Judas betrayed him. (Mark 14 and the other Gospels)*

(77) *The Last Supper. (Mark 14 and the other Gospels)*

(78) *Pontius Pilate. (The Gospels)*

(79) *A Crown of Thorns. (The Gospels)*

(80) *Jesus hung on the cross for six hours. (The Gospels)*

(81) *(a) Jesus was crucified there. (b) Calvary (or the Place of the Skull). (The Gospels)*

(82) *Matthew, Mark, Luke, and John wrote the four Gospels.*

(83) *Luke.*

(84) *Seven loaves and two fishes. When a hungry crowd of thousands faced him, Jesus took the little food available and miraculously turned it into enough to feed them. (Matthew 14:17)*

(85) *Peter. (Matthew 13:28-31)*

(86) *Jesus had four brothers and more than one sister. We learn this in the Gospel According to Mark 6:3: "Is not this the carpenter, the son of Mary, the brother of James, and Joseph, and of Judas, and Simon? And are not his sisters here with us?" (Matthew 13:56, Mark 6:3)*

(87) *A rich man. (Matthew 19:24)*

(88) *It was Jesus who saw Satan fall. (Luke 10:17)*

(89) *Five were wise (those who brought oil), and five were foolish (those who forgot the fuel). (Matthew 25:1)*

(90) *Jesus said these words, which mean, "Father, Father, Why Hast Thou Forsaken Me?" Jesus said these words from the cross, but they were not his last words, which were, "Into His hands I commend my spirit." (The Gospels)*

(91) *The Second Coming.*

(92) *Armageddon. (Revelations)*

(93) *The Book of Revelations, which was written by John.*

(94) *(a) White horse and rider (pestilence), red horse and rider (war), black horse and rider (famine), and pale horse and rider (death). (b) The Four Horsemen of the Apocalypse. (Revelations 6, 7)*

(95) *"Do unto others as you would have them do unto you."*

(96) *Jesus lived thirty-three years. (The Gospels)*

(97) *Jesus raised Lazarus from the dead. He had been dead four days. (John 11, 12)*

(98) *Joseph was descended of the royal line of David. (Matthew, Luke, and John)*

(99) *Parables. Jesus taught by using short, simple, familiar stories, from which a moral or religious lesson could be drawn.*

(100) *The Prodigal Son. (Luke 15)*

(101) *The Sermon on the Mount. (Matthew 5 and the other Gospels)*

(102) *Thomas, one of the twelve apostles, earned the name Doubting Thomas when he was skeptical that Jesus had appeared to other apostles after his death. When Jesus appeared to Thomas and he saw the wounds, he believed in the Resurrection. (The Four Gospels and Acts I)*

(103) *The Beatitudes are the declarations of blessedness pronounced by Jesus in the Sermon on the Mount. Each Beatitude starts with the word "blessed," which is what beatitude means.*

(104) *Salome was known for her Dance of the Seven Veils, which so pleased her stepfather Herod Antipas that he promised her anything she wanted. Salome demanded the head of John the Baptist, who, Salome thought, had offended her mother. (Matthew 14:6-11)*

(105) *"For whatsoever a man soweth, that shall he ALSO REAP." (Galatians 6:7)*

(106) *"Greater love hath no man than this that he LAY DOWN HIS LIFE FOR HIS FRIENDS." (John 15:13)*

(107) *"For what shall it profit a man, if he shall gain all the world and lose HIS OWN SOUL." (Matthew 16:26)*

(108) *"What doth your lord require of thee, but to do justly, and to love mercy, and to WALK HUMBLY WITH THY GOD?" (Micah 6:8)*

(109) *"A time to love , and a time to hate; a time of war, and A TIME OF PEACE." (Ecclesiastes 3:1)*

(110) *"A man hath no better thing under the sun than to eat, and to DRINK, AND TO BE MERRY." (Ecclesiastes 15, and Isaiah 22:13)*

(111) *"Vanities of vanities; all is VANITY." (Ecclesiastes 1:2)*

(112) *"There is nothing new UNDER THE SUN." (Ecclesiastes 1:9)*

(113) *The King James Version is read by many more people than any other.*

(114) *(b) The Pentateuch (meaning the first five).*

(115) *Genesis, Exodus, Leviticus, Numbers, and Deuteronomy are the first five books of the Bible.*

(116) *John Wycliffe (c. 1393).*

(117) *William Tyndale.*

(118) *The Old Testament is much longer.*

(119) *Women could not read the Bible, unless they were "noble or gentle women."*

(120) *The Old Testament contains thirty-nine books. The New Testament contains twenty-seven books.*

(121) *Both the Old Testament and the New Testament were first written in Hebrew.*

(122) *(a) The Dead Sea Scrolls, the oldest known copies of the Old Testament, other religious writings, laws, and poetry written between 200 B.C. and A.D. 50, were discovered in what is now the Israeli-occupied West Bank. (b) They were found in a cave.*

(123) *Song of Songs.*

(124) *The Book of Esther.*

Greek to Me: Gods and Goddesses

Myths are loved by both philosophers and children. They were, perhaps, the first fairy tales—fantastic stories created by people to explain the mysteries of their world, to teach lessons, and to change human behavior. Some myths have a playful, happily-ever-after quality. Some are cruel. Some are challenging. Most attempt to explain the otherwise inexplicable, and to give some order to elements of our lives that appear irrational.

Myths deal with the fundamentals of human life: birth, death, love, hate, jealousy, passion, vanity, selfishness, greed. These were abroad in the universe in the Golden Age of Greece, as they are in our own. The gods and goddesses of my-

thology interfere with human actions; they intermingle and interbreed with humans. They can be seen both as busybody characters in stories and as objectifications of human psychological traits.

Today, the religions of ancient Greece and Rome are dead; not a living soul worships the gods of Mount Olympus. But to understand the rich allusions that have been passed down through Western literature, we must be acquainted with them.

❶ Let's start with a Matching Question about the most important Greek gods and goddesses. See if you can match the Greek gods and goddesses to their titles. For extra credit, give the Roman equivalents.

God/Goddess	Title
1. Aphrodite	**(a)** God of Science and Commerce (Messenger)

(Continued on the next page.)

God/Goddess	Title
2. Athena	**(b)** God of Fire or Forge
3. Ceres	**(c)** Goddess of the Moon and of the Hunt
4. Hera	**(d)** God of Love
5. Zeus	**(e)** God of Wine and Music
6. Hermes	**(f)** King of the Gods of Olympus
7. Hephaestos	**(g)** Queen of the Gods of Olympus
8. Eros	**(h)** God of War
9. Artemis	**(i)** God of the Sea
10. Dionysus	**(j)** God of the Underworld
11. Ares	**(k)** Goddess of Grain and Crops
12. Poseidon	**(l)** Goddess of Wisdom
13. Hades	**(m)** Goddess of Love

❷ According to most accounts of the Creation in Greek mythology (though there are many), in the beginning there was Chaos. Floating on the disorder of Chaos was an orderly egg. The egg (whose name, Nox, means Night), burst open, and from it were born five elements. Can you name them?

❸ As the Creation story continues, Earth and Sky mated and produced twelve super-gods. What was this group of gods called?

4 Ten of these super-gods married one another. Two of them, Cronus and Rhea, had three sons of supreme importance to Greek myth. Who were they?

5 The family of Cronus and Rhea suffered a great deal of in-fighting, but eventually the three wrangling sons gained dominion over sky, sea, and underworld. Which son took over the sky, which one the sea, and which became king of the underworld?

6 What high ground did the gods call home?

7 To pass back and forth between heaven and earth the gods entered through a gate swung open by the four Seasons. What was the gate made of?

8 King Zeus often called the gods to a great hall of the palace where they feasted. What did they eat and drink at these feasts?

9 The waitress or cup-bearer who brought this meal was the goddess of youth. She was the wife of Hercules, and she had the power of making the aged young again. Who was she?

10 For dinner music, one of the gods played his lyre, while the nine Muses

sang. Can you name this god who gave music to the mortals and bore a musician son, Orpheus?

11 The Greeks thought the earth was shaped like a disk. They considered Greece to be in the middle of the earth and that the central point of Greece was a small city on the side of Mount Parnasses, famous for the temple of Apollo and its oracle. Name the city.

12 The oracle mentioned in the preceding question was the most celebrated of Grecian oracles. How did people communicate with this oracle who gave answers in riddles?

13 The gods lived in houses made of brass; they wore shoes of gold. Which of the gods made both?

14 Zeus founded the Olympic games at Olympia in 776 B.C. They were repeated every fifth year, and they lasted for five days. How many athletic competitions were held, and what were they?

15 The gods and goddesses visited earth often, and they sometimes had romantic relationships with mortals. Helen of Troy, for example, considered the most beautiful woman in the world, was the product of a bizarre mating between a god and a mortal. Who were Helen's parents?

16 The union in the preceding question produced three other offspring as well; one figures prominently in Greek mythology. Can you name Helen's sister, the unfaithful wife of Agamemnon, who with her lover murdered her husband?

17 Athena also had a strange birth; she sprang full grown from the forehead of her father. Who was Athena's father?

18 To create daylight, one of the gods drove a chariot of fire across the sky. Which of the gods performed this daily task? Was it (a) Hephaestos, (b) Icarus, or (c) Apollo?

19 The god in the preceding question typifies one side of the Greek ideal, order and reason. His half-brother typifies the other side—wild, creative energies. Who is this infamous god who loves wine, women, and song?

20 In classical art, Zeus is depicted carrying a weapon with which he zapped those whose attention he wanted. What was this weapon?

21 Lesser divinities of nature, these beautiful maidens had power over certain natural phenomena such as springs and rivers, trees and woods, mountains and sea. What were these lovely maidens called?

22 A three-headed dog guarded the gate to the underworld. He welcomed those who entered and devoured those who tried to leave. Was the dog's name (a) Medusa, (b) Lethe, or (c) Cerberus?

23 Another odd creature in mythology was the Centaur. He had the head of a man, but the body of an animal. What was the animal?

24 Many-headed monsters and various creatures abound in Greek mythology. A pair of them lived on either side of the Strait of Messina. On one side was a sea monster in the shape of a whirlpool. On the other side was a horrible six-headed monster who lived in the cliffs. As ships tried to avoid the whirlpool, they came close to the cliffs, only to have the six-headed monster promptly pluck six sailors, one for each mouth, and chew them up. Can you name this dynamic duo?

25 Not many seafarers who ran up against the charming couple mentioned in the preceding question lived to tell the tale, but two particularly famous warriors did. Who were they?

26 Can you match the following famous transgressors with their punishments in the underworld?

Punishment	Transgressor
1. Eternally push a rock up a hill only to have it roll back down on him	**(a)** Prometheus
2. Stand forever hungry under a bough filled with fruit that he could never reach	**(b)** Sisyphus
3. Tied to a rock for eternity, while vultures ate at his liver	**(c)** Ixion
4. Tied to a huge wheel on which he was destined to turn forever	**(d)** Tantalus
5. Slew bridegroom on wedding night and for punishment was confined to the underworld forever to pour water from a leaky jar.	**(e)** Daniad

27 Hercules was given a number of labors to perform. One was to kill a lion with an impervious hide; another was to behead the Hydra, a many-headed monster. In total, how many labors did Hercules have to perform?

28 A beautiful youth, Narcissus, while bathing in a pond, looked into it and fell in love. With whom did he become enamored?

29 A nymph saw Narcissus bathing and fell so in love with him that, from then on, she repeated everything he said. Who was the nymph?

30 We all know the tragic story of Oedipus, who unknowingly killed his father and married his mother. Oedipus had two daughters. One was named Ismene. Who was the other: (a) Elektra, (b) Antigone or (c) Atalanta?

31 Who was the leader of the Argonauts who went in search of the Golden Fleece?

32 Hera, Athena, and Aphrodite had a great dispute over an object that was inscribed, "To the Fairest." What was this object?

33 Paris was called on to arbitrate the argument—to decide which goddess was the fairest. Hera offered him power if he chose her. Athena offered him military success. But Aphrodite made him an offer he could not refuse. With what did Aphrodite tempt him?

34 With what prize was Paris actually awarded?

35 Achilles was a great Greek warrior, but he had one weak spot. What was it?

36 We've all heard of the Trojan horse. For a three-part question: (a) who built it, (b) who hid in its belly, and (c) what purpose did it serve in the Trojan War?

37 Two people tried to warn the Trojans about the Trojan horse. One was a woman who always told the truth, but whom no one believed. Was she (a) Cassiopia, (b) Cheops, or (c) Cassandra?

38 The Trojan War lasted ten years. Who won, the Greeks or the Trojans?

39 The greatest of all mythological prophets was born a man but became a woman, so he was seen as having the broadest life experience of all Greek figures. Was he (a) Hermaphroditus, (b) Laocoon, or (c) Tiresias?

40 In the modern vernacular, we sometimes say such things as "The benefit performance was held under the aegis of the Metropolitan Club." In Greek mythology, what was an aegis: (a) a wing (b) a banner, or (c) a breastplate?

41 Amazons were large, warlike women who, according to some myths, lacked one significant physical property. What was this?

42 In mythology, ugly, birdlike creatures that swarm around the head of a transgressor are avenging spirits that punish crimes by laying guilt trips on transgressors. What were these maddening creatures called?

43 The three Fates, in charge of spinning and cutting the thread of life, sit by Zeus on his throne and advise him about how to deal with mortals. What are their names?

44 Daphne, the daughter of a river god, wished to remain chaste. She called on her father to help her flee the advances of Apollo. The father helped his daughter by giving her a different form. Did he turn Daphne into a (a) laurel tree, (b) white bird, or (c) raindrop?

45 Which of the following pairs were tragic lovers whose fate was similar to that of Romeo and Juliet: (a) Odysseus and Penelope, (b) Pyramus and Thisbe, or (c) Paris and Helen?

46 Who went into the underworld to find his father, and what did he carry with him?

47 What one-eyed creature imprisoned Odysseus and his men during their voyage back to Greece after the Trojan War?

48 What birds with long claws, pale faces, and the heads of maidens were sent by the gods to torment selected mortals: (a) Harpies, (b) Chimera, or (c) Circe?

49 To whom did Zeus give the task of creating the first Greek man by kneading earth and water together?

50 Who was the first Greek woman, counterpart to the biblical Eve: (a) Io, (b) Pandora, or (c) Cassandra?

51 There was a great flood in Greek mythology, and Mount Parnassus was covered with water. One couple survived. Were they: (a) Pyrrha and Deucalion, (b) Troilus and Cressida, or (c) Paola and Francesca?

52 The Greek "Noahs" in the question above, who survived the flood, had no ark, no animals, no sons or daughters, but they were able to renew the race. How did they do it?

53 Who asked this riddle: What animal is that which in the morning goes on four feet, at noon on two, and in the evening upon three: (a) Sphinx, (b) Centaur, or (c) Gorgoyla?

54 Who was the only person to correctly answer the riddle above, and what was the answer?

55 Zeus became angry with mortals and, as punishment, sent Pandora to earth with a container filled with plagues and evils. When she lifted the lid, all flew out except one small creature who stayed inside. Who remained inside Pandora's jar?

56 Daedalus was a craftsman who wanted to flee with his son from the island of Crete. Daedalus built wings of wax and

feathers for them, but the son, though warned by his father, flew too close to the sun. The wax wings melted, causing the son to fall into the sea and drown. Who was this son who did not obey his father's warnings?

57 Theseus was an Athenian prince sent to Crete to kill a monster that had a man's body and a bull's head. The monster lived in a maze in the basement of King Minos's palace. What was this monster called?

58 King Minos's daughter helped Theseus kill the monster. For a two-parter: (a) what was her name, and (b) how did she help Theseus?

59 Young girls were often the prizes, helpmates, or motivating forces for boys, men, and gods in Greek myths. This beautiful maiden was tied to a rock by Poseidon, king of the sea, to punish her vain mother. She was rescued by Perseus. Who was she?

60 Which goddess fell in love with Adonis, the most handsome mortal?

61 This young girl, the daughter of Demeter, was kidnapped by Hades and forced to marry him. She ate six pomegranate seeds in the underworld, which changed the weather of the world above. Can you name her?

62 A king of Cyprus made a statue of a beautiful woman with which he fell in love. After he kissed the statue, it came alive. What was the name of this king, and what did he name the statue?

63 Midas was a greedy king who wished that everything he touched would turn to gold. The god, Dionysus, granted the king's wish. But the wish turned into a curse when the king touched something already precious to him. What did King Midas's touch turn to gold?

Answers

① *1(m) Venus (Aphrodite), Goddess of Love. 2(l) Minerva (Athena), Goddess of Wisdom. 3(k) Demeter (Ceres), Goddess of Grains and Crops. 4(g) Juno (Hera), Queens of the Gods of Olympus. 5(f) Jupiter (Zeus), King of the Gods of Olympus. 6(a) Mercury (Hermes), God of Science and Commerce (Messenger). 7(b) Vulcan (Hephaestos), God of Fire or Forge. 8(d) Cupid (Eros), God of Love. 9(c) Diana (Artemis), Goddess of the Moon. 10(e) Bacchus (Dionysus), God of Wine and Music. 11(h) Mars (Ares), God of War. 12(i) Neptune (Poseidon), God of the Sea. 13(j) Pluto (Hades), God of the Underworld.*

② *The five elements were day, light, love, sky, and earth. The egg burst open, creating light and day, separating earth from sea, and sky from both. The lightest part sprang up and formed the skies; the air was next in weight and place. The earth, being heavier, sank below. Water took the lowest place and buoyed up the earth. (Notice that while love is one of the five elements, hate is not. Hate, jealousy, pride, and other passions were born along with the first gods.)*

③ *Titans. When earth and sky mated, the sky fertilized earth with its showers, and the first gods, or Titans, were born.*

④ *These brothers were Zeus, Poseidon, and Hades.*

⑤ *Zeus, King of the Gods, held dominion over the sky. Poseidon took over the sea, and Hades came to rule the underworld.*

⑥ *Mount Olympus, an actual mountain in Greece, was home to Zeus, Hera, and their offspring. Some say, however, that the gods lived in a mysterious place above Mount Olympus, not on the mountain itself.*

⑦ *Clouds.*

⑧ *They ate ambrosia and drank nectar. These foods were composed mainly of flowers and honey from flowers. Those who ate ambrosia became immortal.*

⑨ *Hebes. (Today we might call her a nutritionist to the gods.)*

(10) *Apollo. Perhaps best known as the god of poetry, prophecy, medicine, and light, Apollo was also the leader of the Muses to whom Mercury gave the lyre he invented.*

(11) *Delphi. Travelers came from far and wide to consult the Delphic oracle.*

(12) *At first they communicated with the oracle by shouting into the cleft in the side of the mountain out of which an intoxicating vapor flowed. Soon, however, a temple to Apollo was erected near the site, and a priestess, Pythia, was seated on a tripod placed over the chasm from which the divine vapors flowed. Pythia was appointed to inhale the hallowed air, which inspired the cryptic words she uttered to those who came to consult the oracle. Priests then interpreted her words.*

(13) *Hephaestos, god of metalwork and fire, made both the houses and shoes of the gods. Hephaestos is probably better known by his Roman counterpart, Vulcan.*

(14) *There were five competitions: running, leaping, javelin-throwing, wrestling, and throwing the quoit (or boxing).*

(15) *Leda, a princess, and Zeus, in the form of a swan, were Helen's parents. To escape his wife Hera's jealousy, Zeus disguised himself as a swan so he could mate unnoticed with the mortal Leda (in an act commemorated by W.B.*

Yeats, in his poem "Leda and the Swan"). Thus, Helen, the most beautiful woman on earth was born from the union of a god, a graceful beast known to have a nasty temperament, and a mortal.

⑯ *There are several contradictory versions of this event, but in most of them Leda hatched Helen and three more offspring from two eggs. One of the other offspring was Helen's sister, Clytemnestra, who, after the Trojan War, murdered her husband, Agamemnon, the king of Micenea.*

⑰ *Athena is also the daughter of Zeus. Zeus had seven wives. His first wife, Metis, was predestined to bear a daughter, Athena, and then a son who would overthrow Zeus. Zeus did not care for this plan, so he swallowed Metis while she was pregnant with Athena to ward off the birth of a rebellious son. When it came time for Metis to give birth, Zeus developed a bad headache, and Athena sprang forth from his forehead fully grown. Wisdom, thus, was born out of the forehead of a god—near, of course, his thinking mechanism, the brain. No one seems to care about what happened to the swallowed wife.*

⑱ *(c) Apollo, God of the Sun (twin brother of Artemis, Goddess of the Moon), drove the chariot of fire across the sky to create daylight.*

⑲ *Dionysus (the Romans usually called him Bacchus) is the son of Zeus and a Theban princess, Semele. He is the god of wine, and represents the energy and excitement of animal impulses, life, and growth. The story of his birth is unusual. Hera, the wife of Zeus, became angry when she heard that her husband's lover Semele was with child. Disguised as a crone, Hera went to Semele and told her that Zeus was not a god but an imposter. Semele demanded that Zeus appear to her in godly radiance to prove himself. When he did, Semele was burned to death by his brilliance. But Zeus, not to be thwarted, took her unborn son from her and sewed the baby up in his thigh to continue gestation. So when Dionysus was born, he was a child of both the loins and the thigh of Zeus. He had a double dose of sexuality, and often drove women into frenzies.*

⑳ *Zeus is usually seen carrying a thunderbolt shaped like two cones. As the father of gods and men, he is depicted as majestic, mature, bearded, sometimes enthroned, and sometimes carrying a scepter. In ancient art, Zeus is often accompanied by an eagle, his sacred bird, and he may be wearing a breastplate.*

㉑ *These maidens were called nymphs. Dryads were tree nymphs; Naiads, water nymphs; Oceanids and Nereids, sea nymphs; and Oreads, mountain nymphs.*

㉒ *(c) Cerberus was a hideous, three-headed dog that guarded the entrance to the underworld where Hades, Prince of Darkness, lived.*

(23) *Centaurs had horses's legs, bodies, and tails, and the heads, arms, and breasts of a human. The Centaurs were noisy, drunken troublemakers, wild and boisterous. Only one, Chiron, was a decent Centaur. He was wise and gentle and tutored Achilles and Jason.*

(24) *This couple was Scylla, the sailor-eating monster who resided in the cliffs, and Charybdis, who sucked in and discharged the sea three times a day in a frightful whirlpool.*

(25) *Odysseus (Ulysses) and Aeneas, with the help of the gods, escaped the clutches of Scylla and Charybdis. Scylla was turned into a rock and is said still to lie in the Strait of Messina awaiting unwary mariners.*

(26) *1(b) Sisyphus pushed the rock, 2(d) Tantalus (from which comes the word "tantalize"), stood under the fruit tree, 3(a) Prometheus stole fire (probably meaning mental powers and consciousness of self) and gave it to mortals for which he paid with his liver, 4(c) Ixion, who tried to seduce Hera, was tied to a wheel in Tartarus (the lowest part of the underworld), 5(e) Daniad—there were several—who killed her bridegroom, attempts to pour from a continuously leaky jar.*

(27) *Hercules performed twelve labors, but the exact description and chronol-*

ogy varies. He is usually depicted as a muscular giant in a lion skin with a club. When Hercules slays monsters, this often symbolizes a purification of the world; evil powers flee. His strength is employed for good purposes.

(28) *Narcissus fell in love with himself when he saw the reflection of his beautiful face in a clear pool. (From him is derived the word "narcissist" to describe self-involved people.)*

(29) *Echo, a nymph, fell in love with the beautiful, conceited Narcissus. Her name, of course, is given to repetition in nature.*

(30) *(b) Antigone was Oedipus's other daughter. For a long and wonderful tale about them read Sophocles's play* Antigone. *(Elektra, by the way, was Oedipus's sister. Atalanta appears in other Greek myths.)*

(31) *Jason led the Argonauts on a search for the Golden Fleece. On the trip he met and married the sorceress Medea who eventually murdered her own children to punish Jason for leaving her for another woman. (It is on the incantations of Medea that Shakespeare modeled the lines of the three witches in* Macbeth.*)*

(32) *The three goddesses fought over a golden apple, which was meant for the fairest woman in the land. The argument started at a wedding celebration to which all the gods and god-*

desses were supposed to be invited. One name was left off the list: Eris, Goddess of Strife. Undone by the social cut, Eris tossed a golden apple in a window to create mischief. She certainly succeeded. In fact, the Trojan War may be traced back to Eris's reaction to this event. (Those who addressed the invitations tried to exclude Strife from the wedding, but then, even as today, strife cannot be eliminated completely!)

(33) *Aphrodite offered Paris the most beautiful woman in the world. Paris chose love and beauty, even in the face of kingship and military power.*

(34) *Helen, the daughter of Leda and Zeus, was the prize. But Helen was married to King Menelaus of Sparta, so Paris had to kidnap her. When he did, Greeks from far and wide set out to avenge the disgrace of the king and reclaim Helen ("the face that launched a thousand ships"). Thus began the Trojan War.*

(35) *Achilles' heel was his one weak spot. When his mother, Thetis, went to dip him in the river Styx, a "baptism" that would make him invulnerable, she held him by his heel, so it never became wet. As luck would have it, Achilles, the greatest warrior on the Greek side in the Trojan War, was struck in the heel with an arrow from Paris's quiver. It was a fatal blow. (Today, an "Achilles heel" refers to a weak spot in a person's character.)*

(36) *(a) The Greeks built the Trojan horse to trick the Trojans. (b) The greatest Greek warriors hid in the belly of the large hollow, wooden horse. (c) They hid there in order to jump out and kill the Trojans when they came to examine the peculiar creature, a decoy left them as a gift. (From which derives the warning: "Beware of Greeks bearing gifts.")*

(37) *(c) The Trojan princess Cassandra tried to warn the Trojans of the trick, but no one believed her. Why? The ever-youthful womanizer, Apollo, had once fallen in love with Cassandra and had given her the gift of prophecy. But when she spurned him, he cursed the gift: she would always speak the truth, but she would never be believed.*

(38) *The Greeks won. At night, while the Trojans celebrated their seeming victory over the Greeks with food and wine, the Greek warriors came out of the wooden horse, entered the gates of the city, and attacked the slumbering Trojans. The Greeks burned Troy, killed the enemy, and won the long war.*

(39) *(c) Tiresias is the blind prophet, an important figure in Greek mythology. He was born a man but was turned into a woman when he came upon two snakes mating and killed the female snake. He was a woman for seven years; then he came upon an identical scene, and this time he killed the male snake. He was turned into a man*

again. Because of his double nature, he was called on to settle an argument between Zeus and Hera about whether the man or the woman received the most satisfaction from sex. When he said that the woman's enjoyment is far greater, Hera struck him blind. To make up for his blindness, Zeus gave him the gift of prophecy.

(40) *(c) An aegis was a breastplate of Zeus made by the God of Fire and Forge, Hephaestos. From this protective breastplate, we derive the use of the word "aegis" to mean "under the protection or sponsorship of."*

(41) *They lacked a right breast. According to some myths, Amazons cut off their right breasts so their breastplates would fit more snugly, enabling them to take better aim with their bows. Amazon, in fact, means "breastless." (However, in ancient art, these hardy women are represented as being normally endowed. So you never know whom to believe. Also, nobody mentions the left-handed Amazons.)*

(42) *The Furies—hideous swarming creatures who caused wrongdoers to suffer from guilt. They were supposed to punish those whose misdeeds fell between the cracks of what we know as legal justice. The Furies could drive a person mad.*

(43) *Atropos, Clotho, and Lachesis were the three Fates in charge of spinning and cutting the threads of life. Clotho is the spinner;*

she spins the threads of human life. Lachesis is the disposer of lots; she determines the length of the thread of human life. Atropos means inflexible. She severs the thread of human life.

(44) *(a) Daphne's father, Peneus, a river god, turned her into a laurel tree.*

(45) *(b) Pyramus and Thisbe were neighbors. They fell in love but their parents objected. The two managed to talk through a crack in the wall of the house. One day they agreed to meet in the forest. Pyramus arrived and found a bloody veil. Thinking Thisbe was dead, he killed himself. Seeing his body, she then killed herself. This myth is amusingly burlesqued in Shakespeare's* A Midsummer Night's Dream.

(46) *Aeneas was the Trojan hero featured in Virgil's* Aeneid, *which describes his adventures in his search for a new home after the fall of Troy. When he reached the shores of Italy, he consulted Sibyl, a prophetess, about visiting the place of the dead to get advice from his father, Anchises. She instructed him to find a golden branch in the forest and take it with him to help him return to earth. Sibyl warned Aeneas: "The descent to the Underworld is easy; the gate of Hades stands open night and day; but to retrace one's steps and return to the upper air, that is the toil, that is the difficulty."*

(47) *The Cyclops. The Cyclopses were a gigantic and barbarian race of shep-*

herds in Sicily, who devoured human beings. Each had one circular eye in the middle of his forehead. One of the Cyclopses imprisoned Ulysses and his men in a cave, but Ulysses was able to trick the Cyclops and blind him with a fiery poker, so that he and his men could escape.

(48) *(a) Harpies. These nasty creatures were sent by the gods to torment a certain Phineus, whom Zeus had punished by striking blind. When a meal was placed before Phineus, the Harpies darted down from the air and grabbed it. Jason and the Argonauts drove them away. (Circe, by the way, was a sorceress who turned Ulysses's men into swine when they visited her island, Aeaea. Chimera was a fire-breathing monster, part lion, part goat, and part dragon.)*

(49) *Zeus gave Prometheus (whose name means forethought) the task of making the first man. He did so by kneading together earth and water. Prometheus pitied the poor ignorant humans he created, so he stole fire from the gods and gave it to them. He is credited with giving mortals the power to think. Punished for stealing the fire, he was chained to Mount Caucasus, where a vulture preyed on his liver. Eventually, he was rescued by Hercules. Prometheus's brother, Epimetheus (which means afterthought), took on the special chore of creating animals.*

(50) *(b) Pandora was the first Greek woman, often compared to Eve. She is the*

*sister of Prometheus. Literally, her name means all (*pan*) gifted (*dora*). She was given every gift by the gods, but when she was entrusted with a box (most myths say a jar) and instructed not to open it, her curiosity got the best of her. She raised the lid and out flew all the ills of humankind.*

(51) *(a) Pyrrha and Deucalion survived. Just as the biblical God became disgusted with humankind and decided to destroy the world in a great flood, in Greek mythology, Zeus, displeased with the earth's creatures, announced his intention to destroy them. He let loose the rivers and poured them over the land. Pyrrha and his wife Deucalion found refuge on the top of Mount Parnassus and proclaimed that they would renew the race.*

(52) *When Zeus resolved to do away with humankind, Prometheus, the father of Deucalion, warned Deucalion and his wife Pyrrah, instructing them to build a raft to float above the destruction. After many days they came to rest on top of Mount Parnassus. There they consulted an oracle, asking how to renew the race. The oracle, as usual, spoke cryptically: the two were to throw their mother's bones over their shoulders. This puzzled the Greek "Noahs" for a bit, but at length Deucalion reasoned that the mother of all is Ge (Earth). Ge's bones must be stones. The two survivors of the flood tossed stones behind them, and the objects grew soft and assumed human shapes. The stones Deucalion threw*

sprang up as men; Pyrrha's stones sprang up as women. Thus was the race renewed.

(53) *(a) The Sphinx, an awful creature with the body of a lion and the torso of a woman, asked this riddle of everyone on the road to Thebes. If they failed to answer the riddle correctly, the Sphinx killed them.*

(54) *Oedipus solved the riddle with this answer: "Man, who in childhood creeps on hands and knees, in manhood walks erect, and in old age with the aid of a staff." The Sphinx was so humiliated that she cast herself down from the rock and died.*

(55) *Hope alone remained inside Pandora's container. Whether Zeus was withholding hope from humankind, or reserving hope for humankind, is an unresolved question.*

(56) *Icarus was the son who did not heed his father's warning and was drowned.*

(57) *The monster was called the minotaur.*

(58) *(a) Ariadne. (b) The king's daughter was upset by the beast that lived below her and feasted on fourteen Athenians each year. One of the Athenians fated for its jaws was the handsome Theseus. Ariadne consulted Daedalus, who had built the labyrinth in which the minotaur lived, about how to help Theseus escape from the maze. She*

was given a ball of thread, which she gave to Theseus who unwound it through the passages and found his way out after killing the minotaur.

(59) *(b) The Ethiopian princess, Andromeda. Perseus had just slain a hideous monster called Medusa, when he came across Andromeda on the rock. He quickly dispatched the second monster. Perseus still held the head of the slain Medusa, which was so ugly that anyone who looked on it would turn to stone. (Perseus had escaped this fate himself by looking at Medusa's reflection in his shield.) Perseus rescued Andromeda, and was about to claim her as his wife when one of her old suitors, Phineus, came along. Perseus held up the head of Medusa and Phineus became a chunk of granite.*

(60) *Aphrodite. Adonis, who loved to hunt, was gored to death by a wild boar. Aphrodite wept bitter tears over his untimely death. Her tears mixed with the blood of Adonis, and where it touched the ground beautiful red anemones sprang up. Alas, the anemone, like Adonis, is short-lived. Called the Wind Flower, its blossoms are opened by the wind, which then whisks them away. Percy B. Shelley uses this myth as the basis of his pastoral elegy on John Keats's death,* Adonais.

(61) *Persephone. The daughter of Demeter, Goddess of Grains and Crops, refused to eat and became pale and thin in the underworld.*

Back on earth, her mother neglected her crops as she searched for her daughter. Just as Persephone was about to die of starvation, Hades pressed six pomegranate seeds into her mouth—a deceitful act, because the law of the underworld was that one who eats anything there must stay forever. But Zeus struck a deal with his brother, Hades: since Persephone ate only six pomegranate seeds, she would stay in the underworld only six months a year, and she would stay above with her mother the other six. (And that is how we came to have seasons: six months of dearth and darkness while Persephone is below with Hades, and six months of sun and growth while she is above.)

(62) *Pygmalion was a king who refused to marry until he could find a maiden as lovely as the statues he sculpted. Once he made the most beautiful statue of all and called it Galatea. Pygmalion fell in love with Galatea, put his arms around her, and kissed her cold lips. At once the marble grew warm and color flowed into it. The two were married and had a son Paphos. (George Bernard Shaw based his* Pygmalion *on this myth. Later, in the Lerner and Lowe musical,* My Fair Lady, *Pygmalion became Henry Higgins, and Galatea, Eliza Doolittle.)*

(63) *King Midas was pleased with the wish granted him by Dionysus until his little daughter threw her arms around him and was immediately turned into gold.*

To Be or Not to Be an Expert on Shakespeare

The name William Shakespeare is probably known to every schoolchild. It's likely that any person of any nationality who has sat in a classroom can quote a line or two from the Bard's thirty-seven or thirty-eight works for the theater (the precise number is in some dispute). Shakespeare is widely regarded as among the two or three most important dramatists in history. Except for the Bible, his are the most often quoted works of literature.

More facts are recorded about Shakespeare than any other playwright of his time except Ben Jonson. But there are gaps—and various students of literature have filled the gaps with myth and speculation.

To begin, let's attempt to sort out some of the facts about the life of William Shakespeare from the myths.

1. Myth or fact. Shakespeare was born on April 23, the same day—52 years later—that he died.

2. Myth or fact. For several years, Shakespeare was a country school teacher.

3. Myth or fact. Shakespeare's first child was born six months after his marriage?

4. Myth or fact. The "dark lady" mentioned in Shakespeare's sonnets was Queen Elizabeth?

5. Myth or fact. Shakespeare was homosexual.

6. Myth or fact. While scholars have traced eighty-three different spellings of the name Shakespeare, Shakespeare himself spelled his name four different ways and pronounced it "Shaxpere."

7. Myth or fact. Shakespeare did not go to college.

8 Myth or fact. Only a few years after his death, Shakespeare had no direct descendants.

9 Myth or fact. A popular appellation for Shakespeare is "The Bard of Avon." This name was suggested by the town in which the poet was born.

10 Myth or fact. Shakespeare was married at 18, became a father at 19, and fathered twins at 20.

11 Myth or fact. In 1592, Shakespeare's play *Henry VI* was the hit of the London theater season.

12 Myth or fact. Shakespeare's mother was Mary Arden; his wife was Anne Hathaway.

13 Myth or fact. Shakespeare wrote his own epitaph, which reads: "Blessed be the man that spare these stones And cursed be he that moves my bones."

14 Myth or fact. Shakespeare lived during the reigns of both a queen and a king.

15 Let's try a Matching Question next. See if you can match the character to the play in which he or she appears.

Character	Play
1. Duncan	**(a)** *King Lear*
2. Iago	**(b)** *Macbeth*
3. Bolingbroke	**(c)** *Othello*
4. Goneril	**(d)** *Hamlet*
5. Nurse	**(e)** *Richard II*
6. Hector	**(f)** *Richard III*
7. Cassius	**(g)** *Romeo and Juliet*
8. Ophelia	**(h)** *Julius Caesar*
9. Octavia	**(i)** *Troilus and Cressida*
10. King Edward IV	**(j)** *Antony and Cleopatra*

See if you can identify the Shakespearean characters suggested below.

16 In *Julius Caesar*, who is "the noblest Roman of them all"?

17 In The *Merchant of Venice*, who demands "a pound of flesh"?

18 What are the names of the three fairies in *A Midsummer Night's Dream*? Are they (a) Helena, Diana and Violenta, (b) Adrian, Luciana, and Emilia, or (c) Pease Blossom, Mustard Seed, and Cobweb?

19 Who is the woman in *The Merchant of Venice* who dresses as a judge?

20 Two Franciscans, Lawrence and John, intervene in the love affair of

Romeo and Juliet. These two have the same religious title. What is it?

21 Who is Julius Caesar's closest friend?

22 In *A Midsummer Night's Dream*, who pours magic juice into Titania's eyes and makes her fall in love with a "donkey"?

23 Who is Hamlet's mother, the Queen of Denmark?

24 In *Hamlet* what two men jump into a grave and begin fighting?

25 In *A Midsummer Night's Dream*, who is king of the fairies? Is it: (a) Bottom, (b) Oberon, or (c) Lysander?

26 Whose ghost does Hamlet see?

27 In *Julius Caesar*, who has a "lean and hungry look"?

28 Which of Shakespeare's Richards is called "crook-back"?

29 Julius Caesar's wife, Calpurnia, begs him not to go outside on what day?

30 Shakespeare's three greatest villains appear in *Othello*, *King Lear*, and *Richard III*. Can you name them?

31 Three Shakespearean characters, all female, seem to die or be killed, but subsequently return to life. They are found in *Pericles*, *Cymbeline*, and *The Winter's Tale*. Are they: (a) Ophelia, Rosalind, and Isabella, (b) Kate, Tamora, and Anne, or (c) Thasia, Imogen, and Hermoine?

32 By what other name is Henry, Prince of Wales, called in *King Henry IV*?

33 What villainous character kills Lady Anne's husband and father, then seduces her to prove that he can do anything he wants?

34 What character dies from a snake bite?

35 What shipwrecked princess sees no man but her father for sixteen years?

36 What play features "the Moor of Venice"?

37 What character in *Measure for Measure* is asked to give up her chastity for the life of her brother, Claudio?

38 "A savage and deformed slave," half-man, half-beast, speaks these words: "Be not afraid. The isle is full of notes, sounds, and sweet airs/That give delight, and hurt not." Name the play and the character.

39 In one of Shakespeare's plays, a father comes to a brothel and recognizes that it is his daughter who has been sent to minister to him. Is he (a) Pericles, (b) Prospero, or (c) Timon of Athens?

40 The *Two Gentlemen of Verona* are (a) Valentine and Proteus, (b) Antonio and Panthino, or (c) Orsino and Sebastian?

41 *Two Gentlemen of Verona* contains two sets of lovers. Which of these couples is not in that play: (a) Julia/Proteus, (b) Silvia/Valentino, or (c) Portia/Shylock?

42 What Egyptian uses the expression "my salad days"?

43 Who is Shakespeare's famous "mutual pair"?

44 In what play do we find these simple folk: Quince, Snug, Flute, Snout, and Starvling?

45 By what other name do we know the mischievous Puck?

46 What Shakespearean "heavy" undergoes a ducking, a beating, and a burning in *The Merry Wives of Windsor*?

47 What are the names of King Lear's daughters?

48 Name the two feuding families in Romeo and Juliet.

49 How old is Juliet, according to her father?

50 Here are some more characters to match with the plays in which they appear.

Character	Play
1. MacDuff/Duncan	**(a)** *Macbeth*
2. Ariel/Prospero	**(b)** *Henry IV*, Parts I and II
3. Regan/Cordelia	**(c)** *King Lear*
4. Mariana/Isabella	**(d)** *Othello*
5. Polonius/Laertes	**(e)** *The Tempest*
6. Desdemona/Iago	**(f)** *Romeo and Juliet*
7. Tybalt/Mercutio	**(g)** *Hamlet*
8. Sir Toby Belch/ Viola	**(h)** *Twelfth Night*
9. Falstaff/Henry, Prince of Wales	**(i)** *Measure for Measure*

Now let's see how much you know about the London theaters in Shakespeare's time.

51 In 1598 the Lord Chamberlain's Men pulled down their theater and carried the timbers across the Thames to build a new theater on Bankside. Shakespeare was one of the shareholders of the new theater. What was its name?

52 What epidemic intermittently caused the closing of London theaters during Shakespeare's life?

53 A flag flown from the turret of the Globe Theatre indicated that a performance was to take place that day. What different messages were conveyed by the flying of (a) a black flag, (b) a red flag, and (c) a white flag?

54 The first theatrical company Shakespeare was associated with was the Lord Chamberlain's Men. In 1603 this company took a different name What was it?

55 In Elizabethan drama, who played the female roles?

56 Those in the audience who stood in the yard around the stage paid an entry fee of one penny. Commonly called "groundlings," they also had another, more pungent, name. What was it?

57 Shakespeare created Richard III, Hamlet, Othello, King Lear, Antony, and Coriolanus for a great tragedian, who was also a major shareholder in the Lord Chamberlain's Men, Shakespeare's company. Was the renowned thespian (a) Thomas Pope, (b) Will Kempe or (c) Richard Burbage?

58 What happened to the Globe Theatre on June 29, 1613?

59 What respected official ran the brothels around the Globe, Swan, and Rose theaters during Shakespeare's time?

60 Besides theaters, in what other locations were plays performed in Shakespeare's London?

61 Here is a quiz about the titles of Shakespeare's plays. See how many you can answer.

(a) How many plays have "Richard" in the title?

(b) What play's title begins and ends with the same word?

(c) The second word in this play's title is also the last word in the title. What is that four-letter word?

(d) What play has a season in the title?

(e) What play announces that it's a comedy?

(f) What play has a three-word title, each word beginning with the letter "L"?

(g) Only one play has "you" in the title. What is the complete title?

62 In what play are the brothers Dromio of Ephesus and Dromio of Syracuse featured?

63 What war is being fought in *Henry IV, Part III*?

64 In what play are three boxes—one of gold, one of silver, and one of lead—important to the action?

65 In what play does Margaret sound like the Queen of Hearts in *Alice in Wonderland*? She says, "Off with the crown; and, with the crown, his head; And whilst we breathe, take time to do him dead."

66 In four of Shakespeare's plays, a woman dresses like a man. How many of the four women can you name? For extra credit, also name the plays.

67 Which of Shakespeare's historical tragedies begins with this line: "Now is the winter of our discontent"?

68 Let's try a short quiz about the form and presentation of some of Shakespeare's work.

(a) "Easy lies the head that wears a crown." If you were to scan this line, what rhythm, typical of Shakespearean verse, would you find?

(b) Shakespearean characters sometimes talk to themselves ("To-morrow, and to-morrow, and to-morrow," for example). What is the term for that manner of address?

(c) Shakespeare wrote a series of poems consisting of fourteen lines of iambic pentameter. What is the name of the form of these poems?

(d) In his plays, Shakespeare typically writes in a particular verse form. What is it called?

(e) What source for his material did Shakespeare most often use? Can you also name two other frequently used sources?

69 Shakespeare's longest play is the most famous play ever written, and apart from the Bible, it is the most quoted work in the English language. What is it?

70 Which plays are considered Shakespeare's four principal tragedies?

71 What was the first tragedy in the Western world since the fifth-century masterpieces of Aeschylus, Sophocles, and Euripedes?

72 In broad terms, the plays below can be characterized in a word or phrase. See if you can match the description to the appropriate drama.

Description	Play
1. revenge play	**(a)** *Othello*
2. drama of jealous sexual passion	**(b)** *Macbeth*
3. tragedy in which countries are lost through a couple's mutual obsession	**(c)** *King Lear*
4. guilt play	**(d)** *Antony and Cleopatra*
5. tragedy of an historical character with a deformed body	**(e)** *Richard III*
6. drama of greed and filial ingratitude	**(f)** *Hamlet*
7. play in which wrongs of one generation are reconciled in its children	**(g)** *Coriolanus*
8. play about mistaken identities	**(h)** *Romeo and Juliet*
9. tragedy of family feuds and young love gone awry	**(i)** *A Comedy of Errors*
10. political play about a soldier who gets his way by force	**(j)** *The Winter's Tale*

73 What festive ritual, featuring Hippolyta and Theseus, is about to take place in Athens when *A Midsummer Night's Dream* opens?

74 Hippolyta, in the play mentioned above, is queen of what group of strong women warriors?

75 In what fantasy does Theseus say that the lunatic, the lover, and the poet live under the sway of imagination?

76 In what very early (probably 1593) play do these horrors occur: Lavinia enters with her hands cut off and her tongue cut out; she has been "ravish'd" and tortured. A character has his hand cut off, and Lavinia picks it up with her teeth. A character kills the two men who have raped Lavinia, cooks them, and serves them in a pie to their mother, Tamora, Queen of the Goths?

77 In what play does Jacques make the famous "seven ages" speech that begins with "all the world's a stage" and concludes with "Sans teeth, sans eyes, sans taste, sans everything"?

78 Who is the shrew's sweet-natured sister in *The Taming of the Shrew*?

79 This character appears in fourteen out of twenty-five scenes in the play that bears his name; he speaks almost one-third of all the lines, and five of his ten soliloquies come in the first three scenes. His is the longest of Shakespeare's history plays, and longer than any

other of his plays except *Hamlet.* Who is this character?

80 One of Shakespeare's kings is also a poet, which renders him incapable of being king. Who is the Richard who says these lines?

"I live with bread like you, feel want,
Taste grief, need friends; subjected thus,
How can you say to me I am a king?"

81 What villain, out of ambition to be king, kills two young princes—his nephews—in the Tower of London?

82 In *Henry VI, Part II,* the rebel Jack Cade is drawn and quartered. What did this mean in Shakespeare's time?

83 Shakespeare's plays are filled with lovers. The most famous are Romeo and Juliet, followed by Antony and Cleopatra. Here are some less familiar pairs. See if you can match the women in the questions with their correct mates in this list: Ferdinand, Florizel, Benedick, Orlando, Claudius, Demetrius, Lysander.

(a) Hermia and Helena had some trouble getting their lovers sorted out, but each eventually ended up with the man she loved. Hermia loved ______, and Helena ______.

(b) Gertrude, widowed, married her husband's brother far too soon to suit her son. Her second husband was ______.

(c) Rosalind disguised herself as a boy, but was happier when she found one to marry. Her lover was ______.

(d) Perdita loved the prince of Bohemia in *The Winter's Tale*." He was ______.

(e) Beatrice and her beloved made a "merry war" of their courtship. "I will be horribly in love with her," her lover said. He was ______.

(f) Miranda is found on a desert isle by the son of the King of Naples, who falls in love with her. He is ______.

84 What is the official name of Hotspur in *King Henry IV*?

85 In what play does the young King of Navarre and his three attendant lords swear off women entirely and vow to spend three years fasting and studying?

86 What Hostess of the Boar's Head tavern in *King Henry IV*, *Part I*, and *Part II*, appears later in *King Henry V* married to the rascal, Pistol?

87 Let's try some questions about Shakespeare's sonnets, which were printed for the first time in 1609 in London.

(a) How many sonnets did Shakespeare write?

(b) With what kind of unusual title was each sonnet assigned?

(c) The first seventeen sonnets form a series. To whom—in general description—is this series addressed?

(d) A woman is addressed in twenty-six sonnets. What adjective is frequently used to describe her? With what adjective did Shakespeare describe her in his first sonnet to her?

(e) In one sonnet, William Shakespeare uses a shortened form of his own name three times in the first two lines. What short form of his name in the poem also suggests "determination" and "desire"?

(f) In the first line of a familiar sonnet, Shakespeare compares the addressee ("thee") to a day of what season?

(g) In this sonnet, Shakespeare refers to "That time of year. . ./When yellow leaves, or none, or few, do hang/Upon those boughs." To what figurative time of year does he refer?

88 As we mentioned, aside from the Bible, Shakespeare's works are quoted more often than any other. Let's see how many of his lines you recognize. For each, name the play and the character who spoke the words.

(a) "Once more into the breach, dear friend, once more."

(b) "We are such stuff as dreams are made of."

(c) "Et tu, Brutus?"

(d) "What a piece of work is man. How noble in reason. How infinite in faculty."

(e) "A horse! A horse! My kingdom for a horse!"

(f) "Out, damned spot."

(g) "What's in a name?"

(h) "Sweets to the sweet."

(i) "One who loved not wisely, but too well."

(j) "What I have done is almost as bad a thing as killing a king and marrying his brother."

(k) "If it were done, when 'tis done, then 'twere well/It were done quickly."

(l) "Was ever woman in this humor wooed? Was ever woman in this humor won? I'll have her, but I will not keep her long."

(m) "Double, double, toil and trouble,/Fire burn and cauldron bubble."

(n) "Lord, what fools these mortals be!"

(o) "Neither a borrower nor a lender be."

(p) "To be, or not to be: that is the question."

Answers

① *Myth. The exact day of his birth has not been documented. His birth is usually celebrated on April 23, but that is the day he died fifty-two years later.*

② *Myth. This is a legend without basis in fact.*

③ *Fact. On 28 November 1582, the Bishop of Worchester authorized the marriage of "William Shagspere and Anne Hathwey of Stratford." The groom was 18, the bride 26. The birth of a daughter Susanna was recorded in the register of Holy Trinity baptismal records on 26 May 1583.*

④ *Myth. This has been speculated by some literary critics, but has no basis in fact.*

⑤ *Myth. This too is mere speculation, possibly based in part on the fact that many of his love sonnets were written to a man, the Earl of Southampton.*

⑥ *Fact.*

⑦ *Fact. There is no record of the Bard's having attended college.*

⑧ *Fact. Shakespeare had only one grandchild, Elizabeth Hall, who reached maturity. She married twice, first to the playwright Thomas Nash, but had no children.*

⑨ *Fact. Shakespeare was born in Stratford-on-Avon, Warwickshire, England and was called in his later years The Bard of Avon.*

⑩ *Fact. Records of these events in Shakespeare's life exist.*

⑪ *Fact.* Henry VI *was probably Shakespeare's first play.*

⑫ *Fact. Shakespeare's mother, Mary Arden, was the youngest of eight sisters in a well-to-do family. Her father left most of his property to her. Shakespeare married Anne Hathaway who lived in a neighboring town.*

⑬ *Fact. His gravestone may still be seen in Stratford.*

⑭ *Fact. Elizabeth I (1558–1603), and James I (1603–1625); thus he lived during the Elizabethan and Jacobean eras.*

⑮ *1(b) Duncan,* Macbeth; *2(c) Iago,* Othello; *3(e) Bolingbroke,* Richard II; *4(a) Goneril,* King Lear; *5(g) Nurse,* Romeo and Juliet; *6(i) Hector,* Troilus and Cressida;

7(h) Cassius, Julius Caesar; *8(d) Ophelia,* Hamlet; *9(j) Octavia,* Antony and Cleopatra; *10(f) King Edward IV,* Richard III.

⑯ *Brutus, according to Mark Anthony, because Brutus loved Rome and its people more than he loved Julius Caesar.*

⑰ *Shylock, a rich moneylender, demanded the pound of flesh from Bassanio in repayment for a debt Bassanio defaulted on. "Let the forfeit," said Shylock, "Be nominated for an equal pound/ Of your fair flesh, to be cut off and taken/In what part of your body pleaseth me."*

⑱ *(c) Pease Blossom, Mustard Seed, and Cobweb.*

⑲ *Portia, who loves Bassanio, dresses as a judge and outwits Shylock. She will allow the moneylender to take his pound of flesh, but he must not shed one drop of Bassanio's blood in doing so, or he himself will die. In this play, Portia makes the famous "quality of mercy" speech.*

⑳ *The two are friars.*

㉑ *Brutus.*

㉒ *Puck, an impish character, plays a prank on Titania, Queen of the fairies. The magic juice he administers to her makes her fall in love with the first person she sees, which happens to be a workman wearing an ass's head. The "curse" is eventually removed.*

(23) *Gertrude.*

(24) *Though the dispute begins in a grave, in a duel before the court, Hamlet and Laertes fight over Ophelia. Laertes's sword has a poison tip, but Hamlet wrests it from him and kills Laertes.*

(25) *(b) Oberon.*

(26) *His father's.*

(27) *Cassius has a lean and hungry look (and is therefore thought to be untrustworthy).*

(28) *Richard III (formerly Duke of Gloucester) is called "crook-back" by Clifford in IV, iii. Richard III was based on the historical Duke of Gloucester mentioned in Raphael Holinshed's* Chronicles of England, Scotland, and Ireland *(1577); the Duke had a "body greatly deformed, the one shoulder higher than the other."*

(29) *The Ides of March (March 15)—a jinxed day, which indeed it proved to be for Caesar, who was murdered later that day.*

(30) *The greatest villains are Iago, Edmund, and Richard III.*

(31) *(c) Thasia (in* Pericles *she dies at sea but is brought back to life by Cerimon, a physician); Imogen (her wicked stepmother poisons her, rendering her lifeless, but she is not dead, only*

in a coma); and Hermoine in The Winter's Tale *is restored to life by Paulina.*

(32) *Prince Hal.*

(33) *Richard III.*

(34) *Cleopatra puts an asp to her breast and dies from its bite in* Antony and Cleopatra.

(35) *Miranda, in* The Tempest, *sees no man but her father for sixteen years.*

(36) Othello *features this Moor, the title character.*

(37) *Isabella.*

(38) The Tempest *is the play, Caliban the creature.*

(39) *(a) Pericles, in* Pericles Prince of Tyre, *suffers a depression from being on shipboard too long. He goes to a brothel to cure his illness. There he finds a beautiful woman who sings to him, and he discovers her to be his long-lost daughter, Marina.*

(40) *(a) Valentine and Proteus are the two gentlemen of Verona.*

(41) *(c) Portia and Shylock are in* The Merchant of Venice, *and they are not lovers.*

(42) *Cleopatra.*

(43) *Antony and Cleopatra are the mutual pair.*

(44) *These simple folk appear in* A Midsummer Night's Dream.

(45) *Puck is also referred to as Robin Goodfellow.*

(46) *Falstaff is literally the heavy here.*

(47) *Goneril and Regan are the wicked daughters, and Cordelia is the good one.*

(48) *The feuding families are the Montagues and the Capulets.*

(49) *Juliet is thirteen. ("My child is yet a stranger in the world—She hath not seen the change of fourteen years," says old Capulet, her father. I, ii, 12—13)*

(50) *1(a) MacDuff/Duncan,* Macbeth; *2(e) Ariel/Prospero,* The Tempest; *3(c) Regan/Cordelia,* King Lear; *4(i) Mariana/Isabella,* Measure for Measure; *5(g) Polonius/Laertes,* Hamlet; *6(d) Desdemona/Iago,* Othello; *7(f) Tybalt/Mercutio,* Romeo and Juliet; *8(h) Sir Toby Belch/Viola,* Twelfth Night; *9(b) Falstaff/Henry,* Henry IV.

(51) *This famous theater was called the Globe.*

(52) *The bubonic plague frequently closed the theaters.*

(53) *(a) A black flag meant a tragedy was being performed, (b) a red flag meant a history, and (c) a white flag meant a comedy.*

(54) *In 1603, with new royalty on the throne, this company became known as The King's Men.*

(55) *Young boys took the female roles. Women could not appear on the stage.*

(56) *The groundlings were also called "stinkards." They were uncouth, unwashed, and often threw food and other things onto the stage.*

(57) *(c) Richard Burbage, arguably the greatest tragedian of the Elizabethan age.*

(58) *The Globe was destroyed by fire in 1613 when a cannon discharged during a performance of* King Henry VIII *and set fire to thatching, which burned quickly and destroyed the theater. (Everyone fled to safety, though one man's pants caught on fire but was extinguished with a pitcher of beer.)*

(59) *The Bishop of Winchester ran the brothels. (This is a fact. It has not been documented that he ordered nuns to staff the brothels, "obedience" being more important than "chastity.")*

(60) *Plays were also performed in Inn Yards, which were constructed to accommodate dramatic presentations.*

(61) *(a) Two:* Richard II *and* Richard III. *(b)* Measure for Measure. *(c)* All's Well That Ends Well. *(d)* The Winter's Tale. *(e)* The Comedy of Errors. *(f)* Love's Labor's Lost *(g)* As You Like It.

(62) *The Dromio brothers are one of the two sets of twins in* The Comedy of Errors.

(63) *The War of the Roses.*

(64) The Merchant of Venice. *Portia, a rich heiress, has suitors choose one of three boxes, one of which contains her photograph. A correct choice will win Portia's hand in marriage. (The lead box contains her photograph, of course.)*

(65) *Queen Margaret says this in* Henry VI, Part III. *Margaret was King Henry VI's wife.*

(66) *Portia (*The Merchant of Venice*), Rosalind (*As You Like It*), Viola (*Twelfth Night*), and Julia (*The Two Gentlemen of Verona*).*

(67) Richard III *is both the title of the play and the name of the speaker.*

(68) *(a) This is iambic pentameter: Five sets consisting of one stressed and one unstressed syllable. The line is from* Henry IV, Part II. *(b) A soliloquy. (c) A sonnet. (d) Shakespeare usually writes in blank verse in his plays. In a few*

exceptions—Romeo and Juliet's love speeches, for example—he includes sonnets. (e) He most often used the Bible. Two other significant sources were Holingshed's Chronicles *and Plutarch's* Parallel Lives of Illustrious Greeks and Romans.

(69) Hamlet *is the longest of Shakespeare's plays.*

(70) *Shakespeare's four principal tragedies are* Macbeth, Othello, Hamlet, *and* King Lear.

(71) Richard III.

(72) *1(f), 2(a), 3(d), 4(b), 5(e), 6(c), 7(j), 8(i), 9(h), 10(g).*

(73) *The wedding of Hippolyta and Theseus is about to take place.*

(74) *The Amazons.*

(75) As You Like It.

(76) Titus Andronicus.

(77) As You Like It.

(78) *Bianca is the shrew Kate's sister in* The Taming of the Shrew.

(79) *Richard III.*

(80) *Richard II.*

(81) *The evil Richard III.*

(82) *Being drawn and quartered was not pleasant. One was first hanged*

until almost dead. Then the intestines were pulled from the body and cut into twelve bits. "Drawn and quartered" also refers to tying each arm and leg to a different horse and driving the horses in four directions, hence quarters.

(83) *(a) Hermia loved Lysander. Helena loved Demetrius. (b) Gertrude loved Claudius. (c) Rosalind loved Orlando. (d) Perdita loved Florizel (e) Beatrice loved Benedick. (f) Miranda loved Ferdinand.*

(84) *Henry Percy.*

(85) Love's Labor's Lost. *These three young men change their minds, however, when three young ladies make a surprise visit.*

(86) *Hostess Quickly.*

(87) *(a) Shakespeare wrote 154 sonnets. (b) The sonnets were given numbers rather than names. (c) These sonnets were addressed to a beautiful youth. (d) The woman of these sonnets is often called "The Dark Lady." In the sonnets themselves, Shakespeare calls her "black." (e) Will, in Sonnet 135. (f) Summer, Sonnet 18. ("Shall I compare thee to a summer's day?") (g) In Sonnet 73 Shakespeare refers to a man who is aging.*

(88) *(a) Henry V/*Henry V. *(b) Prospero/*The Tempest. *(c) Julius Caesar/* Julius Caesar. *(d) Hamlet/*Hamlet. *(e) King Richard/*Richard III. *(f) Lady Macbeth/*Macbeth.

(g) Romeo/Romeo and Juliet. *(h) Hamlet*/Hamlet. *(i) Othello*/Othello. *(j) Hamlet*/Hamlet. *(k) Macbeth*/Macbeth. *(l) Richard III*/Richard III. *(m) Three Witches*/Macbeth. *(n) Puck*/A Midsummer Night's Dream. *(o) Polonius*/Hamlet. *(p) Hamlet*/Hamlet.

The Play's the Thing

A drama is made to be seen and heard. The playwright uses many resources to capture the audience—theater, actors, music, dance, gesture, pantomime, spectacle, costume, and setting. But the playwright uses words to form his thoughts and plot, so a drama is a form of literature. Like fiction, drama tells a story, and like poetry, it uses language imaginatively. Like all literature, it exists on paper long before and after an actual performance. For example, Shakespeare's plays were first printed in 1623. But since that time, many more people have read his works than have seen them.

Drama (which derives from the Greek word, "to act, to do") developed out of formal religious practices in both ancient Greece and the Middle Ages in Europe. Chants, dialogue, setting, spectacle, and action were incorporated into the rituals and liturgy. The great Greek plays date from the fifth century B.C.*, and theater has been with us in one form or another ever since.*

We'll start with some questions about the earliest forms of drama and then move on through the eras, ending with some questions about contemporary theater.

❶ Two works, one by Aristotle and one by Nietzsche, are generally considered indispensable to an understanding of drama. The one by Frederich Nietzsche is *The Birth of Tragedy from the Spirit of Music* written in 1872. What is the work by Aristotle?

❷ Aristotle cited six elements essential to a play: plot, thought, character, diction, music, and spectacle. Though the list is still serviceable, we no longer consider one of these indispensable to a good play (though it is a part of many). Which of these has become expendable?

❸ What are the "three unities" that distinguish Greek tragedy?

❹ Drama began in Greece, where playwrights came each March to compete in a drama festival. The competitions were held in the first known Greek theater built in the sixth century B.C. on the Acropolis. What is the name of the theater?

❺ A satyr-play (from which we get the word satirical), was a bawdy farce that ended a cycle of three serious plays in Greek drama competitions. It usually burlesqued a mythological figure and employed a chorus of actors dressed in goatskins. What is the only complete surviving example of a satyr-play: (a) *Cyclops*, (b) *Philoctetes*, or (c) *The Birds*?

❻ Name the four most renowned Greek playwrights whose works are still mounted frequently.

❼ The earliest of the Greek dramatists mentioned in the preceding question wrote about eighty plays. For this two-parter: (a) name the playwright, and (b) name two of his most well-known plays.

8 Greek audiences almost always knew the stories in the dramas before they went to see them, because many were based on well-known myths. Though this erodes suspense, it builds a certain kind of tension that mystery and horror story writers and dramatists use today. What is the term that indicates that the audience knows what will happen to the character, but the character doesn't know?

9 What is the word Aristotle used to mean a purification of the emotions of pity and terror through art?

10 In classical drama, what causes the tragic hero's downfall?

11 Speaking of tragic heroes, what is the best known play by Sophocles?

12 The protagonist or featured character in the preceding question had a daughter in another play by Sophocles. This play presented the ethical problem that arises when divine law clashes with human law. What is this play?

13 What do the words "buskin" and "sock" refer to in Greek drama?

14 Greek actors often held large masks attached to sticks in front of their faces when on stage. What purpose did these masks serve?

15 In what comedy by Aristophanes do the women go on a sex strike to force their husbands to stop plotting wars against each other?

16 Though Greek drama concerns characters to whom dreadful disasters occur, what dramatic element never occurs on stage?

17 Literature is traditionally divided into genres or categories. Within each genre (novel, poetry, drama, etc.) are genre subsets. There are four major genres in drama that are familiar to us all. One is comedy. What are the other three?

18 Who was the Theban tragic hero in a drama by Sophocles whose name derived from his swollen foot?

19 Drama has its own language, *climax* and *persona*, for example. What do these two terms mean: *deus ex machina* and *denouement*?

20 What is the term used to mean "overweening pride"—often a tragic flaw of a character in Greek drama?

21 Miracle plays dramatized Biblical stories such as those of Noah and the killing of Abel by Cain. Out of these grew Morality plays that often employed allegory. The finest Morality play that survives from the 1500s is: (a) *Erewhon*, (b) *Everyman*, or (c) *Eden*?

22 Another kind of medieval drama concerned Biblical subjects. These plays were presented in English towns on Church festival days by members of trade guilds and were named for the towns. What was this kind of play called?

23 The characters of Punch and Judy, and Harlequin and Colombine originated in a form of improvised comedy that flourished in Italy in the sixteenth to eighteenth centuries and spread through Europe. What is the name of this dramatic form?

24 The first private theater in England was converted from a former Dominican monastery in 1576. Was the name of this theater: (a) The King's Men, (b) Blackfriars, (c) The Swan, or (d) The Pearl?

25 Elizabethan, or Shakespearean, drama focuses on the role of character, or the inherent traits of the *dramatis personae*. Hamlet, for example, was indecisive, and this trait became a part of the dramatic momentum of the play. In Greek plays, character played a part in the person's success or downfall, but one uncontrollable element was even more important. What was that element?

26 A stock comedy character is an old soldier who brags of his exploits, but who is actually a coward and a scoundrel.

Shakespeare's Falstaff has some of these characteristics, but the name actually comes from the title character in a play by Plautus. Is this character (a) Polonius, (b) Pentheus, or (c) Miles Gloriosus?

27 What is the purpose of a "thunder sheet"?

28 What does "legitimate theater" mean, and how did it come to be used?

29 In the early seventeenth century, Ben Jonson developed a type of comedy called the comedy of humours. The most celebrated examples of this are Jonson's *Every Man in His Humour*, and *Every Man out of His Humour*. This kind of comedy rests on a concept of four body humours, or fluids, that determine personality. One of these is choler that produces the choleric personality. Can you name the other three humours?

30 A French playwright of the seventeenth century wrote psychological dramas in which the action is almost exclusively confined to the mind of his character. Six of his nine tragedies deal with the mental reactions of a female character to a crisis in her life. Who is the playwright? For extra credit, name one of his plays.

31 How did the Restoration affect British theater?

(32) One of the classic examples of Restoration comedy is *The Way of the World*, written in 1700. Who wrote it?

(33) A certain type of play is associated with the Restoration period (1660–1700). Noted for satirizing the behavior of the fashionable leisure class and containing unusually clever and wellborn characters, this kind of theater brought its characters out of the pastoral settings of earlier drama and into the drawing rooms. Can you name it?

(34) A 1664 satire by Molière called *Tartuffe, or the Imposter* was performed at Versailles to the consternation of the audience. The play was banned, and Molière was censured. What was it about the play that caused such a stir?

(35) Nikolai Gogol was Russia's first great novelist and short story writer. His place in drama is based chiefly on one work, a satire on bureaucratic corruption in provincial Russia so strong it made Emperor Nicholas I regret he had not censured it. What was this work that foreshadowed social and political satire of the nineteenth century?

(36) Samuel Butler wrote a Utopian play named *Erehwon*. What does this word mean?

(37) Who is the character in Richard Sheridan's *The Rivals* whose name has

given us a word for a person who perpetually and fearlessly misuses words, usually to a comic effect?

38 Another Sheridan play has characters whose names describe their personalities. For example, there's Sir Oliver Surface, Sir Benjamin Backbite, Crabtree, Careless, Lady Sneerwell and Mrs. Candour. Can you name the play?

39 What is the primary characteristic of a "closet drama"?

40 What genre of drama is almost entirely lacking in intellectual content?

41 The British novelist who wrote *Howard's End* made what has become a famous distinction between story and plot. He said, " 'The king died and then the queen died' is a story. 'The king died and then the queen died of grief' is a plot." Who made this comment?

42 In what two-part drama by Johann Wolfgang von Goethe does the devil first appear as a poodle?

43 What Irish playwright of the nineteenth and twentieth centuries had a wit so sharp it has been given a name?

44 When Nora slammed the door, walking out on her overbearing husband in an 1879 drama, its author became a figure of controversy. For a two-parter: (a) who was the

playwright—rightly called the father of modern drama—who presented a female character who defied convention, and (b) what was the name of the play?

45 What twentieth-century playwright was a Sicilian professor who wrote short stories and novels before turning to the theater in his late forties? (Hint: He is known for injecting psychological analysis into drama.)

46 Name the Irish poet and playwright who, in 1899, founded the Irish Literary Theatre, which became the Abbey Theatre.

47 The play *Riders to the Sea*, by Irish playwright John Millington Synge, contains four major characters: Maurya, Bartley, Cathleen, and Nora. But the most powerful force in the drama, and the one that controls the action and emotion, is not listed in the *dramatis personae*. What is that character?

48 Another of Synge's plays caused a riot when it opened in 1907 at the Abbey Theatre in Dublin. The press of the day reported five hundred policemen outside the theater. What play caused this commotion, and to what did the people object?

49 In Thornton Wilder's *Our Town*, what character directly addresses the audience, narrating the action of the play?

50 *All My Sons* was a successful play by an American playwright; it won the New York Drama Critics Circle Award in 1947. Who was the playwright?

51 A twentieth-century American dramatist wrote stage directions as astonishingly lyrical and vivid as his plays. Here is an example: "Two enormous elms are on each side of the house. They bend their trailing branches down over the roof. They appear to protect and at the same time subdue. There is a sinister maternity in their aspect, a crushing, jealous absorption. . . ." Can you name the playwright?

52 Let's try a Matching Game. Each of the plays in the list on the left has elements of fantasy and allegory. Match the play to its author on the right.

Play	Author
1. *The Birds*	**(a)** Euripedes
2. *Alcestis*	**(b)** Goethe
3. *Dr. Faustus*	**(c)** Maeterlinck
4. *Faust*	**(d)** Ansky
5. *The Dybbuk*	**(e)** Marlowe
6. *The Blue Bird*	**(f)** Aristophanes

53 Name the play considered the masterpiece of the Russian dramatist who also wrote *The Sea Gull*, *Uncle Vanya*, and *The Three Sisters*.

54 Who was the Spanish poet, theater director, producer and designer, who also composed and arranged music, painted, and took a graduate degree in law?

55 Who was the French-Romanian playwright who gave the world "the theater of the absurd" with his *Bald Soprano*? He also gave us these plays: *The Future Is in Eggs*, or *It Takes All Sorts to Make a World, The Killer, The Rhinoceros*, and *The Chairs*.

56 The playwright in the preceding question worked with another dramatist to produce "anti-theater." *Waiting for Godot*, was this dramatist's masterpiece. Who is he?

57 Who was the twentieth-century French existentialist who wrote a one act, four character play set in Hell?

58 What witty play by an Irish-English playwright made the cloakroom in Victoria Station in London the most famous cloakroom in literature? Why was this location important in the play?

59 A German dramatist created ground-breaking literature in *Mother Courage, The Life of Galileo*, and *The Caucasian Chalk Circle*. He employed music, song, masks, commentators, projectors, and grand movement and gesture to push back the limits of western theat-

rical conventions. Ironically, though, his best known character is Mack the Knife, from *The Threepenny Opera*. Who is this playwright?

60 It is no secret that women do not love the author of the naturalistic play *Miss Julie*. A native Swede, this dramatist was possessed of all kinds of manias, and he especially despised women. This attitude pervaded everything he wrote. Yet, in *Miss Julie* (1888), a play in which he set out to create a monster, some room is left for the audience to pity her character. Who was the dramatist?

61 What title character in a poetic drama by Ibsen is careless and compromising, and refuses to face reality as he moves through the play from youth to old age in an existential search for his identity in a world of chaos?

62 In Edward Albee's *The Death of Bessie Smith*, in what act does Bessie appear on stage?

63 What important American political figure is satirized in Barbara Garson's 1966 play *MacBird*?

64 What great playwright wrote a play about a woman who leaves her husband, one about venereal disease, one about a neurotic woman with a gun, and one about an insane old man who falls in love with a young girl and

tumbles to his death from the top of a tower? For extra credit, name each of the plays.

65 Arthur Miller wrote a play about an event in seventeeth-century Salem, Massachusetts. Some have called this a modern morality play because of its strong juxtaposition of good and evil. What is the name of this play?.

66 Tennessee Williams wrote a play that suggested the central characters were cannibalized. What was this play.

67 Who wrote the award-winning 1987 drama, *Fences*, a play about a black family in an urban neighborhood in 1957.

68 For a two-parter: (a) what was the first play given in America by nonprofessional actors, and (b) where was it performed?

69 The first play acted by professional players was at the New Deal Theater, December 6, 1732, in New York City. What was the play and who was the author?

70 What was the first drama to win a Pulitzer prize and who was the dramatist?

71 Who wrote *Four Saints in Three Acts*?

72 What is the stately first name of the playwright of *The Milktrain Doesn't Stop Here Anymore*?

73 Describe the title character in the William Inge play *Come Back Little Sheba*.

74 Name the author of these plays: *What Price Glory?*, *Winterset*, *Key Largo*, *Elizabeth the Queen*, and *Mary of Scotland.*

75 What role did English novelist Virginia Woolf play in the drama *Who's Afraid of Virginia Woolf?* For extra credit, who wrote the play?

76 Here's a two-parter: (a) what twentieth century author, most commonly thought of as a poet, wrote *Murder in the Cathedral*, and (b) whose murder was dramatized in the play?

77 We know that masks were used in Greek drama to help indicate an emotion and to help actors project their voices. What American playwright used them in a 1926 play to depict changes in character? For extra credit, name the play.

78 Let's try another two-parter: (a) who was *The Man for All Seasons*, and (b) who wrote the play about him?

79 Who was the English novelist and playwright ultimately responsible for the musical drama *Cabaret*?

80 An American playwright worked as a contract writer for MGM Studios in 1943, turning out scripts that were never filmed. During this time, he wrote *The Gentleman Caller*, an original screenplay. He later turned it into a successful Broadway drama. Who is the playwright and what was the name of the play?

81 Name the play and playwright of a drama in which God (called "De Lawd") is the chief character.

82 For whom are the characters Estragon and Vladimer still waiting?

83 The father of what twentieth-century playwright was a famous actor noted for the lead in *The Count of Monte Cristo*? For extra credit, what screen actor did this playwright's daughter marry?

84 What play by an American playwright contains these characters: Big Daddy, Maggie the Cat, and Brick?

85 Name the play by Archibald MacLeish that was based on the Book of Job.

86 Who were the two minor characters from a Shakespearean play that contemporary British dramatist Tom Stoppard borrowed for the title characters in a play of his own?

87 What drama, adapted from a novel by John Steinbeck, appeared on the New York stage for the first time in 1990 and featured the Joad family?

88 What Irish playwright—he later wrote *Endgame* and *Happy Days*—went to Paris in the 1920s and became James Joyce's secretary?

89 Maxwell Anderson's drama *Winterset* was based on a famous court case in which an old judge who sentences a couple to death goes through life tortured because he thinks he has committed a miscarriage of justice. Eventally driven mad by guilt and grief, the judge becomes a bum who lives under the Brooklyn Bridge. Who were the two the judge sentenced to death?

90 Another drama set in a courtroom is *Inherit the Wind*. On what famous trial is this play based?

91 What Eugene O'Neill play takes place in the summer of 1912 in the backroom of Harry Hope's saloon, where Rocky is the night bartender?

92 The one-woman play *The Belle of Amherst* was based on the life of what American poet?

93 What American play of the twentieth-century is set in the home of the

Younger family—Mama, Beneatha, Walter Lee, Ruth and Travis—and deals with the social theme of racial inequality?

94 *The Night of January 16* by Ayn Rand, produced in New York in 1935, boasted that for the first time in history the audience could dictate the ending of a play. Jurors, who were paid three dollars for their services, were selected from the audience at each performance. Two endings for the courtroom melodrama were available, and the jury could choose either. In a more recent play, adapted from an unfinished novel by Charles Dickens, the audience was given the option of selecting the culprit in the who-dun-it. Can you name this play?

95 The 1938 skit *Limitations of Life*, by Langston Hughes, satirized an earlier play whose characters—a Negro mammy and a tragic mulatto—Hughes considered stereotypes. What was the play, and who was its author?

96 Who wrote *The Devil and Daniel Webster*?

97 These characters are in search of a play by Tennessee Williams: Hannah, Nono, Shannon, and Maxine. What is the play?

98 What contemporary playwright has written these dramas with historical figures: *Harriet Tubman—The Second Moses, Crispus Attucks*, and *I Have a Dream*?

99 In what drama is a prep school student unjustly suspected of homosexuality?

100 This great American playwright, author of *Long Days Journey into Night*, requested this inscription on his tombstone: "There is something to be said for being dead." Name the playwright.

101 Maurice Barrymore and Georgiana Drew had three famous children connected with the theater. Can you name them?

102 What drama about poverty in the Southern backwoods, first produced in New York in 1933 and based on a novel by Erskine Caldwell, takes place on the farm of Jeter Lester on a country road in Georgia?

103 Name the Mary Chase play—a combination of fantasy and farce in which the central character is a white rabbit that never appears onstage—that won a Pulitzer Prize and ran for 1,775 performances on Broadway.

104 Neil Simon's second Broadway play, produced in 1963, starred Robert Redford, Elizabeth Ashley, Mildred Natwick, and Kurt Kaszner—and a long flight of stairs to the top floor of a New York City brownstone. What was this play?

105 This farcical melodrama, which has become a modern classic, features the Brewster sisters, genteel poison-cup artists. It opened on Broadway in 1941 and ran for five years. Name it.

106 What is the name of the two-character comedy by Bernard Slade that was a long-running play on Broadway about two married people, who don't happen to be married to each other, but who meet each year for twenty-five years for a tryst?

107 *Angel Street* by Patrick Hamilton, opened in New York City in 1941. A thriller starring Vincent Price about a man trying to drive his wife mad by tampering with the lighting, it had another title when it opened in London. That title was used again in the later film production. What was the title?

108 Name the author of *The Buried Child, Cowboy Mouth*, and *The Tooth of the Crime*.

109 Moss Hart collaborated on plays with George S. Kaufman, Cole Porter, and Irving Berlin. Which of these plays did he write with Kaufman? Was it (a) *Jubilee*, (b) *Face the Music*, (c) *You Can't Take It with You*, or (d) *Dinner at Eight*?

110 The popular and prolific contemporary American playwright, Neil

Simon, has written many Broadway hits. Can you name his first play?

111 Angelina Grimke was the first black woman to write a play performed by an all-black cast. The year was 1916. What was the play?

112 Let's try a Matching Game. Match the playwright to the play.

Playwright	Play
1. Harold Pinter	**(a)** *The Effect of Gamma Rays on Man-in-the-Moon Marigolds*
2. Eugene Ionesco	**(b)** *The Lark*
3. Sean O'Casey	**(c)** *The Zoo Story*
4. Clare Boothe	**(d)** *A Taste of Honey*
5. David Mamet	**(e)** *A Month in the Country*
6. Paul Zindel	**(f)** *American Buffalo*
7. Lillian Hellman	**(g)** *The Birthday Party*
8. Jean Anouilh	**(h)** *The Rhinoceros*
9. Ivan Turgenev	**(i)** *The Little Foxes*
10. Shelagh Delaney	**(j)** *The Plough and the Stars*
11. Jean Genet	**(k)** *The Balcony*
12. Edward Albee	**(l)** *The Women*

113 What is the longest running play in the history of the English-speaking stage, and who wrote it?

Answers

① *Aristotle's* Poetics, *written in the fourth century* B.C.

② *Music is no longer an essential element in drama.*

③ *Time, place, and action. This means that the action depicted takes place in a span of twenty-four hours or less in a single place. The single action has no subplots.*

④ *The Theatre of Dionysus was the birthplace of Western drama.*

⑤ *The only surviving example of a satyr play is the* Cyclops *of Euripedes.*

⑥ *The foremost Greek playwrights are Aeschylus, Sophocles, Euripedes, and Aristophanes. The first three wrote tragedies; Aristophanes was the greatest ancient Greek writer of comedy.*

⑦ *(a) Aeschylus (525–456* B.C.*) was the earliest writer of Greek tragedy, whose plays still exist in complete form (but only seven of his eighty plays have come down to us intact). (b)* Agamemnon *(part of the* Oresteia *trilogy) and* Prometheus Bound *are the most well-known of his plays.*

⑧ *This is called dramatic irony; the audience knows the fate of the character and the tension builds as we watch the character learn.*

⑨ *Catharsis.*

⑩ *The classical tragic hero has a "tragic flaw"—some character trait that interacts forcefully with his or her environment to bring the hero low. This trait can be stubbornness, passion, curiosity, or any trait in excess. The Greek tragic hero also must hold an exalted office such as king, queen, prince, or high state official, because implicit in tragedy is a fall from a high position.*

⑪ Oedipus Rex *is the best known of Sophocles' plays. In it, Oedipus kills his father and marries his mother.*

⑫ Antigone.

⑬ *The* buskin *(also called the* cothurnus*) was a thick-soled boot worn by actors in Greek tragedy. This made the actor appear larger and more dignified. Since it was never worn in comedy, the term has come to imply tragedy. The* sock *was a soft, light shoe similar to a ballet slipper worn by the classical comedy actor. This footwear allowed the actor to appear smaller and to move quickly, lightly, and with grace.*

⑭ *Because the Greek theaters were so huge (some holding 17,000 people), the actors were often far away from the audiences. The masks usually had expressions of emotion—happi-*

ness, sadness, anger—painted on them, so the audience could see the facial expressions of the characters. Also, the masks operated somewhat like megaphones: they usually had amplifying holes cut in the mouth areas. Of course, these devices made Greek drama somewhat stylized, not unlike the Noh theater of Japan.

⑮ *The* Lysistrata. *Despite the lack of resolve of some of the women, the plan succeeds.*

⑯ *Violence never occurs on stage in Greek drama. When characters are knifed, hanged, or tear their eyeballs out (which frequently occurs), these actions take place behind stage and are reported to the audience and other characters in the drama by a messenger.*

⑰ *The genres of drama are comedy, tragedy, melodrama, and farce.*

⑱ *Oedipus means "swollen foot," and indeed Oedipus suffered this malady for good reason: his feet had been pinned together when he was an abandoned baby hung in a tree. His father, Laius, King of Thebes, had been warned by the Delphic Oracle that his newborn son would eventually kill him. The King left the baby to die, but a peasant found the child and raised him. Many years later, Oedipus killed a man he had encountered on the road. The man was Laius, his own father. Sometime after, Oedipus arrived in Thebes and delivered it of a plague. In gratitude, the townspeople gave him the Queen as his bride. And yes, this bride was his own mother, Jocasta. When Jocasta discovered this, she killed herself, and Oedipus, seized with madness, tore out his eyes and wandered for the rest of his life. (See Sophocles's* Oedipus Rex *for this riveting story.)*

⑲ Deus ex machina *means, literally, "god from the machine." It originally referred to the arrival on stage of a god or other non-mortal figure by means of a mechanical contraption somewhat like a crane. This "god from the machine" carried mortals off to heaven, or Mount Olympus, or otherwise unscrambled their impossibly tangled lives. Later the term came to mean any sudden resolution of a complicated dramatic situation in an arbitrary way, or in a way in which the audience has not been prepared. (For example, a long-lost rich uncle comes in to pay the rent, or a passerby coincidently stops a murder.)* Denouement *literally means "the untying." This is the moment when all the mysteries of the plot are finally revealed. The knots are untied, the murder or mystery solved, and the audience understands "who done it" and why. The denouement usually comes after the climax, or the high point of the drama.*

⑳ Hubris, *which means excessive pride, or arrogance.*

㉑ Everyman. *This Morality play has a universal theme (the "summoning of*

Everyman" before God for an accounting of his life) dramatic structure, and some warm, humorous moments.

㉒ *They were called Mystery plays because they were performed by craft guilds (called "mysteries") in medieval England.*

㉓ *This dramatic form is called* commedia dell'arte. *The performers improvise their material around a loosely conceived, but well-known, plot.*

㉔ *(b) This was Blackfriars Theatre. It was used by Shakespeare's company, The King's Men, after 1608.*

㉕ *Fate. Greek drama is generally "tragedy of fate," in which forces outside the protagonist have an overwhelming role.*

㉖ *Miles Gloriosus is the name for this inflated but cowardly lion.*

㉗ *Little used today, a thunder sheet was a thin sheet of iron that was rattled and shaken to create thunderous sounds behind the stage. Today we use recordings or other high-tech equipment.*

㉘ *This term came into being in the eighteenth century when the licensed theaters in London were attempting to rout out new theaters that were sprouting up. Legitimate drama referred to five-act plays that contained no dancing, singing, or comedy. Today, in the United States, the term refers to the drama of the stage, as opposed to film or television—the "upstarts" of drama.*

(29) *The other humours are black bile for a melancholic, blood for a sanguine, yellow bile for a phlegmatic. The characters and situations in the comedy of humours were comic even to those in the audience who were unfamiliar with Jonson's eccentric theory.*

(30) *Jean Racine. His plays include* Andromache, Phaedra, Berenice, *and* Britannicus, *among others.*

(31) *Charles II was restored to the throne of England, and theaters, which had been closed for fourteen years under a repressive and puritanical regime, were reopened.*

(32) *William Congreve.*

(33) *A comedy of manners.* The Way of the World *is one example; Somerset Maugham's* Our Betters *is another.*

(34) Tartuffe *dealt with religious hypocrisy. Seemingly pious people with whom those in the audience could identify were revealed as hypocrites. Too many of the highborn in the audience saw themselves in the hypocrites on stage. After he was censured, Molière wrote two petitions to King Louis XIV in an attempt to get the ban lifted. The petitions are as amusing as the play itself, and they*

were successful. In August, 1667, Tartuffe *was performed at the Palais-Royal.*

(35) The Inspector-General *(1836), considered by many to be the greatest Russian play.*

(36) Erehwon *is "nowhere" spelled backwards. ("Utopia" means "nowhere" in Greek.)*

(37) *Mrs. Malaprop, from whom we get malapropisms (which means "things out of place.")*

(38) *This Sheridan play is* The School for Scandal.

(39) *Closet drama is drama written to be read rather than performed.*

(40) *Farce. The purpose of farce is to provoke uncomplicated hilarity. Because content and wit are subordinated to grotesque physical action, farce is often referred to as "low comedy."*

(41) *E.M. Forster.*

(42) *In* Faust *Mephistopholes first appears as a poodle. (The Greek word for "cynic" is "dog," and the wily devil appears as both cynic and dog.)*

(43) *George Bernard Shaw, who had Shavian wit. Shaw wrote five novels in addition to some forty plays. He was a debater and*

orator, wrote polemical essays, and was both a music and drama critic.

(44) *(a) The playwright is Henrik Ibsen; (b) the play is* A Doll's House. *The controversy arose because European theater in the nineteenth century had become merely entertainment, and theater-goers were accustomed to plays that reinforced middle-class conventions, which this play did not do.*

(45) *Luigi Pirandello (1867-1936), who wrote* Six Characters in Search of an Author *in 1922.*

(46) *William Butler Yeats.*

(47) *The sea—the controlling force of the drama—into which all the male characters ride to their deaths.*

(48) The Playboy of the Western World *caused this scene. W.B. Yeats said that people rioted because they objected to new ideas presented by the play.*

(49) *The Stage Manager addresses the audience directly.*

(50) *Arthur Miller. His greatest triumph, however, came in 1949 with* Death of a Salesman.

(51) *Eugene O'Neill. These are the stage directions to* Desire Under the Elms.

(52) *1(f)* The Birds, *Aristophanes; 2(a)* Alcestis, *Euripedes; 3(e)* Dr. Faustus, *Marlowe; 4(b)* Faust, *Goethe; 5(d)* The Dybbuk, *Ansky; 6(c)* The Blue Bird, *Maeterlinck*

(53) The Cherry Orchard, *by Anton Chekov.*

(54) *Federico Garcia Lorca, who was taken from his home at dawn, lined up before a wall, and shot with a machine gun in the first month of the Spanish Civil War. No logical reason has ever been given for his execution. Some have speculated that his pen was more terrifying to some than a sword.*

(55) *Eugene Ionesco.*

(56) *Samuel Beckett, a friend and colleague of Ionesco's.*

(57) *Jean-Paul Sartre wrote this play called* No Exit.

(58) The Importance of Being Ernest *is the play; Oscar Wilde is the playwright. The location is important in the play because Jack Worthing, who is sueing for the hand of the daughter of snobby Lady Bracknell, tells the Lady that he was born in a handbag in the cloakroom in Victoria Station. These are hardly the family credentials that Lady Bracknell aspires for in a son-in-law. The play, of course, is a clever social satire dealing with British class structure.*

(59) *Bertolt Brecht (1898–1956), a restless experimenter in drama who tried to break away from the conventions of the theater.*

(60) *August Strindberg.*

(61) *Peer Gynt.*

(62) *Bessie Smith, the great black singer, never appears on stage in this play. She dies in a car accident offstage, and a nurse will not allow her body to be brought into a white hospital.*

(63) *Lyndon Johnson (and Ladybird Johnson). The idea for this brutally satirical play came to the author when, in a slip of the tongue during a speech at an anti-war rally in Berkeley in 1965, she referred to the First Lady of the United States as "Lady MacBird Johnson."*

(64) *The playwright is Henrik Ibsen. His plays alluded to here are:* The Doll's House, Ghosts, Hedda Gabbler, *and* The Master Builder.

(65) *The play is* The Crucible, *a dynamic drama of the Salem witchcraft trials.*

(66) *This is the mystifying play* Suddenly Last Summer.

(67) *The fine contemporary playwright, August Wilson. He won the 1987 Pulitzer Prize in drama for* Fences.

(68) *(a) The play was* Ye Bare and Ye Cubb, *by Philip Alexander Bruce.*

(b) It was performed August 27, 1665, at Accawmack, Virginia. The actors were summoned to appear in court three months later. They were found not guilty of sedition, and Edward Martin who had informed on them was ordered "to pay all the expenses of the presentment."

(69) *This play was* The Recruiting Officer *by British comedy dramatist George Farquhar.*

(70) *The drama* Why Marry? *by Jesse Lynch Williams opened in New York City in 1917. It was originally a novel titled* And So They Were Married. *The Pulitzer was announced by President Nicholas Murray Butler of Columbia University in June 1918.*

(71) *Gertrude Stein.*

(72) *Tennessee (Williams), who was, oddly enough, born in Missisippi.*

(73) *Sheba, the title character in the play, is a dog.*

(74) *Twentieth-century American playwright Maxwell Anderson wrote these and other plays.*

(75) *Edward Albee wrote this play. Woolf had nothing to do with writing it, and in fact was dead by the time it was written. The drama's name echoes the children's story* Who's Afraid of the Big Bad Wolf, *and the name of Woolf*

in the title is meant to suggest an eccentric, independent, suicidal woman— as Virginia was.

(76) *(a) T.S. Eliot, and (b) Thomas à Becket.*

(77) *Eugene O'Neill is the playwright;* The Great God Brown *is the play.*

(78) *(a) Sir Thomas More, and (b) Robert Bolt.*

(79) *Christopher Isherwood wrote* Goodbye to Berlin *(1935) about the rise of Nazism; this was adapted for the stage by John Van Druten as* I Am a Camera *(1951) and as the musical* Cabaret *(1966).*

(80) *Tennessee Williams. The screenplay became the very successful drama* The Glass Menagerie.

(81) Green Pastures *by Marc Connelly, which won the Pulitzer Prize for drama in 1930. This popular religious drama, which takes place in heaven, has an all-black cast and is written in the homespun language of the South.*

(82) *Godot—the character who never comes in Samuel Beckett's 1952 play,* Waiting for Godot.

(83) *Eugene O'Neill's father was the famous "Count." O'Neill's daughter Oona married Charlie Chaplin.*

(84) Cat on a Hot Tin Roof *by Tennessee Williams.*

(85) J.B. *is the play based on the Book of Job. It later became a film.*

(86) *Rosencrantz and Guildenstern, attendant lords to Hamlet, were featured characters in Stoppard's* Rosencrantz and Guildenstern Are Dead. *Hamlet himself is made a minor figure in this clever play in which the two major characters have little to do but wait.*

(87) The Grapes of Wrath.

(88) *Samuel Beckett.*

(89) *Sacco and Vanzetti.*

(90) *The Scopes, or so-called "Monkey," Trial that pitted William Jennings Bryan against Clarence Darrow.*

(91) The Iceman Cometh.

(92) *The American poet Emily Dickinson. William Luce wrote the play.*

(93) A Raisin in the Sun.

(94) *The play was* The Mystery of Edwin Drood. *Dickens wrote this as a serial novel but died before it was completed. In the production of the play in New York City, the audience voted on the ending at each performance.*

(95) *This melodramatic play is* Imitation of Life *by Fanny Hurst.*

(96) *Stephen Vincent Benet.*

(97) Night of the Iguana.

(98) *Aileen Fisher.*

(99) Tea and Sympathy. *Robert Anderson wrote the play.*

(100) *Eugene O'Neill.*

(101) *John Drew Barrymore, Ethel Barrymore, and Lionel Barrymore.*

(102) Tobacco Road *by Jack Kirkland and Erskine Caldwell.*

(103) Harvey.

(104) Barefoot in the Park. *It was later made into a movie starring Jane Fonda and Robert Redford.*

(105) Arsenic and Old Lace, *a play by Joseph Kesselring.*

(106) Same Time Next Year. *This play also became a movie and starred Ellen Burstyn and Alan Alda.*

(107) Gaslight. *The film starred Ingrid Bergman and Charles Boyer.*

(108) *Sam Shepard.*

(109) *(c)* You Can't Take It with You, *perhaps Hart's most frequently performed play.*

(110) *Simon's first play,* Come Blow Your Horn, *was performed in 1961.*

(111) Rachel.

(112) *1(g) Pinter,* The Birthday Party; *2(h) Ionesco,* The Rhinoceros; *3(j) O'Casey,* The Plough and the Stars; *4(l) Boothe,* The Women; *5(f) Mamet,* American Buffalo; *6(a) Zindel,* The Effect of Gamma Rays; *7(i) Hellman,* The Little Foxes; *8(b) Anouilh,* The Lark; *9(e) Turgenev,* A Month in the Country; *10(d) Delaney,* A Taste of Honey; *11(k) Genet,* The Balcony; *12(c) Albee,* The Zoo Story.

(113) *The* Mouse Trap, *which opened in London in 1952 and is still playing. Agatha Christie wrote it.*

[illegible]

[illegible] performed in [illegible]

[illegible] Rachel

[illegible]

[illegible]

[illegible]

[illegible]

[illegible]

[illegible]

[illegible] The Zoo Story [illegible]

[illegible]

[illegible]

All Ye Need to Know about Poetry

Poetry is performance art: One cannot, as a poet reminds us, tell the dancer from the dance. And poets are jugglers; they make a disciplined game of keeping many balls in the air. Poets are also architects; in their works, aesthetic and technique are inseparable. But above all, poets play, and poems are made to give pleasure.

The first poetry was undoubtedly in song, and the first English poet known to us by name is "Widsith," the Wide Wanderer, whose song fragments were recorded so long ago, and so crudely, that no one knows the date. Song is music, sound, rhythm, words, and, of course, these are the basic components of poetry as well.

But poetry is made of many more elements: imagery, allusion, repetition, inversion, symbol, suggestion, incantation. It is born of concrete personal experience, and a satisfied reader re-creates the poet's immediate experience. Poetry takes as its subjects the grand passions of love, hate, greed and jealousy, keen observations of nature, and exalted insights into the workings of God.

Poetry is our most refined and precise way of communicating. It makes demands, but the payoff is well worth the exercise.

Let's begin here with some questions on the earliest English poetry and a few early examples of poetry in other languages.

1 A narrative poem, the oldest of the great long poems written in English, dates from the beginning of the eighth century and tells of the hard, heroic lives of early English people. Some of the characters in the narrative are Hrothgar, Grendel, and Grendel's mother. What is the poem?

2 A twelfth-century historian, working from a book he claimed was the "most ancient book in the British tongue," gave the legends of a certain king their first popular written circulation. Who was the king? For extra credit, who was the historian?

3 What color was the knight who proposed a beheading game in a medieval romance that also includes Sir Gawain?

4 These characters are mentioned in a piece of inspirational literature composed in the latter half of the fourteenth century by William Langland (or Langley): Lady Meed, Piers, Do-well, Do-bet, and Do-best. What is the work?

5 What long narrative poem, written in Middle English, begins with these lines: "Whan that Aprile with his showres soote/The droughte of March hath perced to the roote . . ."?

6 The name "Poet's Corner" was given to a section in Westminster Abbey after the first poet was buried there in 1400. Who was that poet?

7 Plato called the greatest Greek lyric poet, a woman who came from the Isle of Lesbos, "The Tenth Muse." Only fragments remain of her poetry; the longest is seven stanzas of an invocation to Aphrodite. Who is the poet?

8 A famous work written by an Italian poet contains ten tales told by ten people during ten days of the plague in Florence. For a two-parter: (a) what is the poem, and (b) who is the poet?

9 What ancient Greek philosopher banished poetry from his "Ideal Republic," and then went on to write one of the most perfect lyrics ever written: "Star of my life, to the stars your face is turned/Would I were the heavens, looking back at you with ten thousand eyes"?

10 Edmund Spenser wrote *Astrophel* as an elegy for his friend Sir Philip Sidney. On what occasions did he write (a) *Amoretti*, and (b) *Epithalamion*?

11 Who is the ancient Greek who originally told (or sang) the stories of *The Odyssey* and *The Iliad* in poetic form?

12 In 1590 Edmund Spenser published the first three books of his allegorical poem in which he hoped to give a picture of a perfect knight. What was the name of this poem?

13 What major poet and dramatist of the sixteenth-century wrote this stanza: "Come live with me and be my love,/And we will all the pleasures prove/That valleys, groves, hills, and fields,/Woods or steepy mountain yields."

14 Give the name of the sixteenth-century poet who wrote this stanza in response to the poet in the preceding question: "If all the world and love were young,/And truth in every shepherd's tongue,/These pretty pleasures might me move,/To live with thee and be thy love."

15 What sixteenth to seventeenth-century English poet wrote two beautiful songs, "Drink to Me Only with Thine Eyes" and "Come, My Celia, Let Us Prove"?

16 In an epic poem (considered the greatest in the English language), the poet set out to "justify the ways of God to man." What is the poem, and who is the poet?

17 The poet who wrote "A Valediction: Forbidding Mourning" was also the Dean of St. Paul's and often wrote sermons. Who is this metaphysical poet?

18 This seventeenth-century poet, who had a disease that caused curvature of the spine so severe that he could stand only four and one-half feet tall, wrote poems in heroic couplets. One of them is *An Essay on Criticism.* Who is the poet?

19 Let's try a Matching Question. Match the poets to their works.

Work	Poet
1. "To His Coy Mistress"	**(a)** Robert Herrick
2. "To the Virgins, to Make Much of Time"	**(b)** Samuel Johnson
3. "Song: Go and Catch a Falling Star"	**(c)** Robert Burns
4. "The Vanity of Human Wishes"	**(d)** Andrew Marvell
5. "To a Mouse"	**(e)** John Donne

20 Name the first woman poet to publish in colonial America.

21 What seventeenth-century poet wrote *L'Allegro, Il Penseroso,* and *Lycidas*?

22 Shakespeare, Spenser, and Sir Philip Sidney were among the few poets who mastered a certain poetic form. What is that form?

23 Alexander Pope wrote a mock heroic poem ridiculing the world of fashion. What is the name of the poem?

24 For a two-parter, try this: (a) in the shape of what flower was Dante's

Heaven, and (b) how many circles are there in Dante's Hell?

25 What punishment in Hell did Dante give his illicit lovers, Paola and Francesca?

26 Elizabethan poetry was written during the reign of Elizabeth I. During the reigns of what two monarchs were the following written: (a) Jacobean poetry, and (b) Carolinean poetry?

27 Which of these sonnets is not the work of Shakespeare: (a) "That time of year thou mayest in me behold," (b) "Batter my heart, three-personed God," or (c) "Let me not to the marriage of true minds"?

28 Match the lines below to the poets who wrote them. For extra credit, name the poems.

Line	Poet
1. "Gather ye rosebuds while ye may"	**(a)** Thomas Gray
2. "I could not love thee, dear, so much,/Loved I not honor more."	**(b)** Edgar Allan Poe
3. "Because I could not stop for death"	**(c)** Robert Burns
4. "How can we know the dancer from the dance?"	**(d)** Dylan Thomas

(Continued on the next page.)

	Line		Poet
5.	"The curfew tolls the knell of parting day"	**(e)**	W.B. Yeats
6.	"For the moon never beams without bringing me dreams/of the beautiful Annabel Lee."	**(f)**	T.S. Eliot
7.	"so much depends on a red wheel barrow"	**(g)**	William Carlos Williams
8.	"O My luve's like a red, red rose"	**(h)**	Robert Herrick
9.	"Do not go gentle into that good night"	**(i)**	Emily Dickinson
10.	"April is the cruelest month"	**(j)**	Richard Lovelace

29 What English poet of the eighteenth and nineteenth centuries, considered quite mad by some and by others a genius, wrote *The Songs of Innocence and Experience*?

30 In a famous poem of the supernatural, an Ancient Mariner stopped several men on their way to a wedding feast. How many wedding guests were there, and how many did the Ancient Mariner stop?

31 In John Keats' poem, "Ode on a Grecian Urn," what is "all ye know on earth and all ye need to know"?

32 Who wrote a poem containing a "rough beast" that "slouches toward Bethlehem to be born"?

33 What lyrical, but almost incomprehensible, poem did Samuel Taylor Coleridge write in his sleep, while under the influence of an "anodyne"—probably opium?

34 This line, "Tyger! Tyger! burning bright," was written and illustrated by what British poet?

35 The wife of an Irish poet professed a talent for "automatic writing." She wrote lines, in a trance, that she claimed were dictated to her by an unearthly being. The poet sometimes used these lines. Who was the poet?

36 "This is the forest primeval" is the first line of a long poem by an American poet. (a) Name the poem, (b) tell where the setting of this forest is and (c) give the name of the poet.

37 William Wordsworth was called a Lake poet because he came from the Lake District in Northwest England. Can you name another Lake poet?

38 When the first edition of *Leaves of Grass* was published in 1855, the *Boston Intelligencer* gave it this review: "The author should be kicked out from all decent society as

below the level of the brute. He must be some escaped lunatic raving in pitiable delirum." Who was the poet?

39 What long poem by T.S. Eliot is divided into these sections: The Burial of the Dead, The Game of Chess, The Fire Sermon, Death by Water, What the Thunder Said?

40 What poet, considered mad in his later years, wrote "Summer is incumen in?"

41 How far was the shot heard in Ralph Waldo Emerson's *Concord Hymn*?

42 According to the poet who wrote about the event, on what date did Paul Revere make his famous ride? For extra credit, name the poet.

43 Do you know why there is "no joy in Mudville"?

44 In "O Captain! My Captain!" whose death does Walt Whitman mourn?

45 What song is sung by the shore of Gicheegumee?

46 John F. Kennedy asked this twentieth-century American poet to read a poem at his inauguration in 1961. The sun's glare prevented the poet from reading the poem he had written for the occasion. Instead he recited

"The Gift Outright" from memory. Who was the poet?

47 What contemporary American poet worked most of his life in the legal department of an insurance company in Hartford, Connecticut to support his poetry habit?

48 Name the American poet who once threw out the first ball of the season for the New York Yankees.

49 For a two-parter: (a) what poet used the word "tintinnabulation" in a poem, and (b) can you name the poem?

50 Can you name what comes on "little cat feet"?

51 What contemporary poet was discovered by Vachel Lindsay when the young poet was a busboy in a Washington hotel and left a packet of his poems next to Lindsay's plate?

52 What stands "under the spreading chestnut tree"?

53 What poet wrote a poem with Muhammed Ali called "A Poem on the Annihilation of Ernie Terrell," a fighter with whom Ali had scheduled a match?

54 Who wrote "next to of course god america i"?

55 Who said, "Speak for yourself, John"? For extra credit, what was the occasion?

56 Name the poet who wrote the following stanza, and the poem from which it comes. "The snail's on the thorn;/God's in his heaven—/All's right with the world."

57 Who are three poets from New England named Lowell?

58 Name the creature that rested on a bust of Pallas and repeated one pessimistic word in a poem by Edgar Allan Poe.

59 Whom or what was the poet addressing when he said, "Hog Butcher for the World/Tool Maker, Stacker of Wheat/ Player with Railroads and the Nation's Freight Handler"? For extra credit, name the poet and the poem.

60 *Green Groweth the Holly* was written by a British monarch who lived between 1491 and 1547. Who was he?

61 What reclusive American poet wrote these lines: "A bird came down the Walk/He did not know I saw—/He bit an Angle-worm in halves/And ate the fellow, raw. . ."?

62 Who is the author of "To an Athlete Dying Young," and "Terrence, This Is Stupid Stuff"?

63 Let's try another Matching Game. Match the poem with the poet.

Poem	Poet
1. *Christabel*	**(a)** Randal Jarrell
2. *The Marriage of Heaven and Hell*	**(b)** Gwendolyn Brooks
3. "The Darkling Thrush"	**(c)** Robert Browning
4. *Ode to a Nightingale*	**(d)** e.e. cummings
5. "The Noiseless Patient Spider"	**(e)** Theodore Roethke
6. *To a Skylark*	**(f)** Percy Bysshe Shelley
7. "My Last Duchess"	**(g)** Denise Levertov
8. "Tell all the Truth but tell it slant—"	**(h)** W.B. Yeats
9. "Not Waving but Drowning"	**(i)** Stevie Smith
10. "in Just"	**(j)** William Blake
11. "The Death of the Ball Turret Gunner"	**(k)** Thomas Hardy
12. "My Papa's Waltz"	**(l)** Samuel Taylor Coleridge
13. "The Circus Animals' Desertion"	**(m)** John Keats
14. "O Taste and See"	**(n)** Walt Whitman
15. "We Real Cool"	**(o)** Emily Dickinson

64 What poet took the road "less traveled by," and what was the name of the poem?

65 "I am the master of my fate/I am the captain of my soul." What is the name of the poem from which these lines come? For extra credit, who wrote the lines?

66 Here's a two-parter: (a) who wrote: "How do I love thee? Let me count the ways" and (b) to whom might we assume she was writing this poem?

67 Supply the missing words here: "I wandered lonely as a cloud/That floats on high o'er vales and hills,/When all at once I saw a crowd,/A host, of ______ ______."

68 How many rode into the Valley of Death in "The Charge of the Light Brigade"?

69 Who, according to Edgar Allan Poe, lived in a kingdom by the sea?

70 How was the evening spread out against the sky in *The Love Song of J. Alfred Prufrock*? For extra credit, who wrote it?

71 Who wrote these words: "T'was brillig, and the slithy toves/Did gyre and gimble in the wabe"?

72 W.B. Yeats wrote a poem about the unusual union that resulted in the birth of Helen, the most beautiful woman in the world. What is the title of the poem, and who were Helen's parents?

73 What American poet who wrote within a strict metrical form said, "I'd as soon play tennis with the net down as write free verse"?

74 What poem by John Greenleaf Whittier (1807–1892) contains these lines: " 'Shoot if you must, this old gray head,/But spare your country's flag,' she said."

75 With what literary and social movement were the poets Allen Ginsberg, Gregory Corso, Laurence Ferlinghetti, William S. Burroughs, and Gary Snyder involved?

76 Langston Hughes speculates that a certain kind of dream may "dry up like a raisin in the wind." What kind of dream is this?

77 For a two-parter: (a) complete this couplet, and (b) name the author: "A poem should not mean/ ______ ______."

78 Which of these poems was not written by Robert Frost: (a) "Mending Wall," (b) "Stopping by Woods on a Snowy Evening," (c) "Sailing to Byzantium," or (d) "Birches"?

79 The following poem by Ezra Pound is in a form often used by Japanese

poets. What is that form? "In a Station of the Metro/The apparition of these faces in the crowd;/Petals on a wet, black bough."

80 *A Child's Christmas in Wales* was written by the poet who wrote "Fern Hill." Who is he?

81 Who is the Victorian author of the lovely, but cynical, poem, "Dover Beach"?

82 Name the Scottish poet who wrote of rustic themes in the vernacular.

83 This English Romantic poet, who died at 26 and had stopped writing because of poor health at 24, left an immeasurable legacy that includes wonderful sonnets and such poems as *Endymion, The Eve of St. Agnes, On Looking into Chapman's Homer,* and *La Belle Dame Sans Merci.* Can you name him?

84 Who wrote a "poetical biography" called *The Prelude*?

85 A nineteenth-century poet's *Bigelow Papers*, political and social lampoons written in the Yankee dialect, established his reputation as a satirist and a wit. Can you name the poet?

86 Who is the Romantic poet who wrote a long poem about Don Juan?

87 Let's try a final Matching Game of contemporary poets. Match poem to poet.

Poem	Poet
1. "Buckdancer's Choice"	**(a)** Theodore Roethke
2. *The Bean Eaters*	**(b)** James Dickey
3. *Harlem Sweeties*	**(c)** Nikki Giovanni
4. *Elegy for Jane*	**(d)** Sylvia Plath
5. *Nikki-Rosa*	**(e)** Dylan Thomas
6. *Daddy*	**(f)** Gwendolyn Brooks
7. *In Memory of Radio*	**(g)** Denise Levertov
8. *Diving into the Wreck*	**(h)** Langston Hughes
9. *Crow Alights*	**(i)** Amiri Baraka
10. *The Force that Through the Green Fuse Drives the Flower*	**(j)** W.H. Auden
11. *In Flander's Field*	**(k)** Ted Hughes
12. *Musee des Beaux Arts*	**(l)** John McCrea

Answers

1 Beowulf, *an anonymous poem written in Old English (or Anglo-Saxon), tells the story of the courageous hero Beowulf, who fights monsters and dragons.*

② *The king is Arthur, and the historian is Geoffrey of Monmouth, Bishop of Asaph (1110–1154), called the Father of English fiction.*

③ *Green. Sir Gawain tangled with the Green Knight in* Sir Gawain and the Green Knight, *an anonymous, unrhymed, romantic verse written in the fourteenth century.*

④ Piers Plowman, *a long poem in alliterative verse composed by Langland or Langley in the Middle Ages. The author was a monk, born about 1331, who continued to add to this poem throughout most of his life.*

⑤ *These are the first lines of "The Prelude" to Geoffrey Chaucer's (1343–1400)* Canterbury Tales.

⑥ *Chaucer was the first poet buried here, and many famous poets have since found their final resting places in "Poet's Corner."*

⑦ *Sappho, the early sixth-century* B.C. *poet. She influenced later poets, such as Catulles, Ovid, and Swinburne.*

⑧ *(a) This was* The Decameron. *(b) The poet is Giovanni Boccaccio (1313–1375), an Italian born in Paris. The long poem, written between 1348 and 1353, is a collection of one-hundred witty tales set against the background of the Black Plague. The work undoubtedly influenced Chaucer, who traveled in both France and Italy.*

⑨ *Plato (427?–347 B.C.), the Greek philosopher.*

⑩ *Sir Edmund Spenser (1552?–1599) wrote the sonnet sequence* Amoretti *in commemoration of his courtship of Miss Elizabeth Boyle, and* Epithalamion *in honor of their marriage in 1594.*

⑪ *Homer, who lived before 700 B.C., wrote both epic poems, the prototype of all subsequent epic poetry.*

⑫ The Faerie Queen.

⑬ *Christopher Marlowe (1564–1593) wrote "The Passionate Shepherd to His Love."*

⑭ *Sir Walter Raleigh (1552–1618), wrote this satirical poem, called "The Nymph's Reply to the Shepherd," in response to the passionate plea of Marlowe's shepherd.*

⑮ *Ben Jonson (1572–1637), English dramatist and poet, included these songs in* The Forrest *(1616), a long poem.*

⑯ *This is the masterpiece of John Milton (1608–1674),* Paradise Lost. *It tells the story of the Garden of Eden, Adam and Eve, and Satan's rebellion against God.*

⑰ *John Donne (1572–1631) was both a poet and the Dean of Saint Paul's.*

⑱ *The small man who wrote heroic verse was Alexander Pope.*

⑲ *1(d) "To His Coy Mistress"/Marvell, 2(a) "To the Virgins. . ."/Herrick, 3(e) "Song"/Donne, 4(b), "The Vanity of Wishes"/ Johnson, 5(c) "To a Mouse"/Burns.*

⑳ *Anne Bradstreet (1612–1672) came to Massachusetts in 1630 with her father Thomas Dudley and her husband Simon Bradstreet; both became governor of the state. She was a dutiful Puritan wife who raised a large family. She also became the first significant woman author in the American colonies.*

㉑ *John Milton.*

㉒ *The form is the sonnet.*

㉓ The Rape of the Lock.

㉔ *Dante Alighieri's* Divine Comedy, *a long vernacular poem of 14,000 lines, is divided into three books: "Paradisio," "Pergatorio," and "Inferno." In the first, (a) heaven is shaped like a multifoliate rose (a rose of many petals). (b) In the "Inferno," Dante's portrait of Hell, there are nine circles, the lowest being Cocytus, the place of traitors.*

㉕ *Paola and Francesca, who became physically attracted while studying a book of poetry together, were consigned by Dante to the Second Circle of Hell, where the lustful reside. Their particular punishment is to cling to each other forever in a sexual embrace, as they are whirled by winds around their circle of hell.*

㉖ *(a) James I (Jacobean), (b) Charles I (Carolinean).*

㉗ *(b) It was John Donne, not Shakespeare, who wrote "Batter my heart, three-personed God." Donne, a metaphysical poet, wrote often about God and other spiritual matters. Shakespeare wrote about mankind and life on earth.*

㉘ *1(h) "To the Virgins, to Make Much of Time"; 2(j) "To Lucasta, Going to the Wars"; 3(i) No. 712; 4(e) "Among School Children"; 5(a) "Elegy Written in a Country Churchyard"; 6(b) "Annabel Lee"; 7(g) "Spring and All"; 8(c) "A Red, Red Rose"; 9(d) "Do Not Go Gentle into That Good Night"; 10(f)* The Waste Land.

㉙ *William Blake (1757–1827), an engraver by trade, was a mystical man. As a child, he saw God looking at him through a window. He also had a vision of the prophet Ezekiel, and saw a tree full of angels. Though thought to be mad by some, he wrote brilliant, deceptively simple poetry. His* Songs of Innocence *include short lyrics, many in the voices of children; his* Songs of Experience *are often about trees, flowers, or animals invested with weariness, illness, or violence.*

(30) *In* The Rime of the Ancient Mariner, *Samuel Taylor Coleridge (1772–1834) tells the story of an old sailor who stops one of three weddings guest to tell him a long, ghostly story.*

(31) *"Beauty is truth, truth beauty, that is all ye know on earth and all ye need to know."*

(32) *W.B. Yeats (1854–1939) wrote this line in his poem "The Second Coming."*

(33) *This poem is the fantastical "Kubla Khan."*

(34) *This is one of William Blake's* Songs of Experience.

(35) *W.B. Yeats' wife claimed to hear voices that instructed her to write certain lines.*

(36) *(a)* Evangeline, *(b) set in Nova Scotia, once called Arcadia. (c) The poet is Henry Wadsworth Longfellow (1807–1882).*

(37) *Samuel Taylor Coleridge also lived in the Lake District.*

(38) *Walt Whitman (1819–1892) is this disreputable poet.*

(39) The Waste Land, *perhaps Eliot's most accomplished work.*

(40) *Ezra Pound (1885–1972) wrote this irreverent poem.*

(41) *In Emerson's poem, the shot was "heard round the world."*

(42) *"On the eighteenth of April in seventy-five." This is the date provided by Henry Wadsworth Longfellow (1807–1882) in his popular poem, "Paul Revere's Ride." The historical date is the nineteenth.*

(43) *"Mighty Casey has struck out." These lines are from "Casey at the Bat," a verse written by Ernest L. Thayer in 1888. Vaudevillian De Wolf Hopper (father of gossip columnist Hedda Hopper) made the verse famous by his theatrical recitations.*

(44) *Whitman mourns the death of Abraham Lincoln.*

(45) The Song of Hiawatha, *by Longfellow, is sung by these shores.*

(46) *The poet who attempted to read in the sun's glare was Robert Frost (1874–1963).*

(47) *Attorney Wallace Stevens (1879–1945) worked in a Hartford insurance company. Some of his poems include "The Anecdote of the Jar," "The Emperor of Ice-Cream," and "Sunday Morning."*

(48) *Marianne Moore*

(1887–1972), an American poet who loved sports, especially baseball.

(49) *(a) Edgar Allan Poe (1809–1849) used this word in his poem, (b)"The Bells."*

(50) *Fog comes in on little cat feet in the poem "Fog," by Carl Sandburg (1878–1967).*

(51) *Langston Hughes (1902–1967), the poet who went on to write "The Weary Blues," "The Negro Speaks of Rivers," "Harlem," and others.*

(52) *The village smithy: "Under the spreading chestnut tree, the village smithy stands." This is the first line from Longfellow's popular "The Village Blacksmith."*

(53) *Marianne Moore. The poem was sent out over the AP wire, much to the surprise of the poet, who confessed that she had never had any work accepted so promptly.*

(54) *e.e. cummings (1894–1962) wrote this poem.*

(55) *Priscilla Alden said this in the 1858 poem,* The Courtship of Miles Standish, *by Longfellow. John Alden has come to ask Priscilla to marry his friend, Miles Standish. This is her reply.*

(56) *Robert Browning (1812–1889) wrote these lines in* Pippa Passes.

(57) *James Russell Lowell (1819–1892) was poet, critic, teacher, and editor. He taught modern languages at Harvard, and was the first editor of* The Atlantic Monthly, *and* The North American Review. *Amy Lowell (1874–1925) was a poet and critic. Her most popular poems are "Patterns," and "Lilacs." Robert Lowell (1917–1977) received the 1947 Pulitzer prize for poetry for* Lord Weary's Castle *and the 1974 Pulitzer prize for poetry for* The Dolphin.

(58) *A raven repeated the word "Nevermore" in the poem "The Raven."*

(59) *Carl Sandburg was addressing the city of Chicago, in his poem "Chicago."*

(60) *King Henry VIII wrote this poem. One of the stanzas reads: "As the holly groweth green/And never changeth hue/So I am, ever hath been/Unto my lady true."*

(61) *Emily Dickinson (1830–1886), a poet who lived in Amherst, Massachusetts, but who seldom left the house.*

(62) *The English poet A.E. Housman (1859–1936) wrote these poems.*

(63) *1(l), 2(j), 3(k), 4(m), 5(n), 6(f), 7(c), 8(o), 9(i), 10(d), 11(a), 12(e), 13(h), 14(g), 15(b).*

(64) *Robert Frost wrote* The Road Not Taken, *whose opening lines are: "Two roads diverged in a yellow wood,/And sorry I could not travel both."*

(65) *"Invictus," by William Ernest Henley (1849–1903).*

(66) *(a) Elizabeth Barrett Browning (1806–1861) wrote this poem contained in* Sonnets from the Portuguese, *and (b) we can assume it was addressed to Robert Browning.*

(67) *. . . "golden daffodils." Wordsworth wrote these famous lines in his poem "I Wandered Lonely as a Cloud."*

(68) *Six hundred rode into the valley of Death in Tennyson's poem.*

(69) *The beautiful Annabel Lee lived in a kingdom by the sea.*

(70) *The evening was spread out against the sky "like a patient etherized upon a table." The poem was written by T.S. Eliot.*

(71) *This nonsense verse from "Jabberwocky" was written by Lewis Carroll (1832–1898).*

(72) *The name of the poem is "Leda and the Swan." Helen, the most beautiful woman in the world, was born from the union of Leda, a mortal, and the god Zeus, who came to her in the form of a swan.*

(73) *Robert Frost, who thought writing poetry within a tight form was a mental exercise.*

(74) *These lines are from "Barbara Frietchie," a fictional encounter in 1863 of the 96-year-old woman and General Stonewall Jackson in Frederick, Maryland. In the poem, the General forbids his Confederate troops to fire on the lady when she produces a Union flag.*

(75) *These poets were associated with the Beat Movement, a generation of artists at odds with their middle-class background. "Beat" was used to mean both worn-out and "blessed" (as in the sense of the beatitudes).*

(76) *"A dream deferred" may dry up like a raisin in the wind.*

(77) *(a) "A poem should not mean/but be." (b) Archibald Macleish (1892–1982) wrote this line in* Ars Poetica.

(78) *(c) "Sailing to Byzantium" was written by W.B. Yeats.*

(79) *This is an adaptation of a Japanese haiku, an unrhymed poem recording the essence of a moment keenly perceived, in which nature is linked to human nature. A haiku usually consists of seventeen syllables in three lines of 5–7–5. Here, Pound uses twenty-eight syllables in three lines of 8–12–8. Nature, and the crowd at the Metro, are closely interwoven in this image.*

(80) *Irish poet Dylan Thomas (1914–1953) wrote both.*

(81) *Matthew Arnold (1822–1888), wrote this poem.*

(82) *This is the work of Robert Burns (1759–1796).*

(83) *John Keats.*

(84) *William Wordsworth.*

(85) *James Russell Lowell.*

(86) *George Gordon, Lord Byron (1788–1824) wrote* Don Juan, *about the legendary Spanish nobleman, notorious for seducing women.*

(87) *1(b), 2(f), 3(h), 4(a), 5(c), 6(d), 7(i), 8(g), 9(k), 10(e), 11(l), 12(j).*

Fiction: A Novel Way to Go

The historian, Geoffrey Arthur (1100–1154) is usually credited as the Father of English Fiction because his History of the Kings of Britain *is more remarkable for its delightful stories than for its historical accuracy. But it was not until 1740 (or 1719 if you consider Defoe's* Robinson Crusoe *the first novel) that the first English novel,* Pamela, *was written by Samuel Richardson. This was followed quickly by Henry Fielding's* Joseph Andrews, *the first example of the English novel as we know it today.*

Of course, fiction had developed, and was continuing to develop, elsewhere as well—in the courts of French kings, for example, among the Celts in

Ireland, and in Italy, Russia, China, and Japan.

Let's see how much you know about the novels and short stories of yesterday and of today, those written in English and those that originated in a foreign tongue.

❶ Considered the first great French novel, this book, published in 1678, involves petty intrigues, schemes, deceits, and flirtations in the glittering court of Henry II.

❷ One of the greatest works of Japanese literature is a novel by Lady Murasaki that consists of six parts. It was probably begun in 1001, but was not translated into English until 1925. What is it?

❸ In what unusual form is *Pamela*, the first English novel, written?

❹ Henry Fielding wrote *Joseph Andrews*, considered the first of the English novels as we know them today. This parody was written in reaction to the work of another writer of that period. Who was he?

❺ What 1767 book by Laurence Sterne contains several blank pages, several totally black pages, uses a stream of consciousness style, and has no plot?

❻ When Gulliver landed in the country of Lilliput, he found the citizens very small. What was their adult height?

❼ What monumental work by Leo Tolstoy documents the affairs of two noble Russian families during the Napoleonic Wars?

❽ Marie Henri Beyle was born in France (1783) and fought with Napoleon. But his great novel, *The Charterhouse of Parma*, was set in Italy. What is the name by which we know the author? For extra credit, what is his other great novel?

❾ Two of Dostoevsky's Karamazov brothers were Dmitri and Smerdyakov. What are the names of the other two—one the skeptic and the other an innocent?

❿ Who is the author of *Moll Flanders*?

⓫ What Polish-born author, who knew no English until he was in his twenties, wrote *The Secret Sharer* and *Heart of Darkness*?

⓬ With the publication of his *Sketch Book* (1819–1920), this writer became the first American author to achieve international fame.

13 Aside from being a name for a modern theater group in Chicago, Steppenwolf was a character in a book by what German author?

14 In a period of seventeen years, what nineteenth-century writer suffering from consumption wrote the following: four volumes of essays, seven of romance, two of the South Seas, three of poetry, five volumes of travel and topography, one volume of political history, and five collections of fantastic tales, including *The Strange Case of Dr. Jekyll and Mr. Hyde*?

15 Samuel L. Clemens chose the pen name Mark Twain. What earlier occupation supplied him with this pseudonym?

16 Who became famous for his colorful stories about the American West that were published in 1870 as the collection *The Luck of Roaring Camp and Other Sketches*?

17 From what novel do these lines come: "Fifteen men on the Dead Man's Chest/Yo-ho-ho and a bottle of rum"?

18 A bit of tricky logic referred to in a novel about World War II went like this: The only way a recruit could get out of the miserable armed forces was to plead insanity. But by desiring with all his heart to get out of the miserable armed forces, one was judged *ipso facto* sane. What was this rule called?

19 The occupation of Eugene Gant's father in Thomas Wolfe's *Look Homeward, Angel* plays an important part in the theme and title of this novel. What does Mr. Gant do?

20 What author wrote a novel in which the main character writes a column of advice for the lovelorn? For extra credit, name the novel.

21 How did the thieves die in *Ali Baba and the Forty Thieves*? Were they (a) boiled in oil, (b) suffocated in a cave, or (c) killed in a duel?

22 What Tolstoy character killed herself by leaping under a train?

23 Who is the nineteenth century writer who wrote several novels about Bertie Wooster and Jeeves?

24 Two talkative creatures wrote notes on Don Marquis's typewriter at night after the writer had finished for the day. Name the famous cockroach and cat who bedeviled Marquis.

25 When a popular Jazz Age American novelist remarked to another famous novelist that "the rich are different from us," the second author replied: "Yes. They have more money." Who were the novelists?

26 The name of Tom Joad's sister is probably derived from a mispronunciation of a flowering shrub. What is her name, and what is the name of the novel in which she appears?

27 Who is the Danish writer beloved by children for *The Ugly Duckling*, *The Emperor's New Clothes*, *The Tinder Box*, and other stories?

28 "All animals are equal, but some animals are more equal than others" is the slogan of a character in a twentieth-century novel. For this three-parter: (a) whose slogan is it, (b) what novel is it from, and (c) who is the author?

29 Who wrote naturalistic short stories about the frustrations of contemporary life, published in the collections *The Triumph of the Egg* and *Winesburg, Ohio*?

30 What is the name of the Edith Wharton novel, set in the 1870s, that gives a satirical portrait of New York society?

31 What fifty-thousand-word novel by Ernest Vincent Wright contains no letter *e* except in the author's name?

32 Who wrote an acclaimed 1969 novel called *Naked Came the Stranger* that was published under the name of Penelope Ashe?

33 Who is the creator of Emma Woodhouse, the strong-willed young Victorian woman in an English novel of manners that bears the heroine's name?

34 The author of *Buddenbrooks* and *The Magic Mountain* also wrote the better-known novel *Death in Venice*. Can you name him?

35 What novel by Dickens contains many autobiographical details, particularly of the author as a boy?

36 The longest sentence in an American novel consists of 823 words and takes up three pages. Can you name the novel and the novelist?

37 *The Last Tycoon*, which has a Hollywood setting, is an unfinished novel by what famous American writer who spent his last years boozing and writing unsuccessful screenplays, tended by the Hollywood gossip columnist Sheila Graham?

38 *The Well of Loneliness* was a controversial American novel of the 1930s by Radclyffe Hall. What made it so controversial?

39 "riverrun, past Eve and Adam's, from swerve of shore to bend of bay, brings us by a commodius vicus of recirculation back to Howth Castle and Environs." This is the

first sentence of James Joyce's novel *Finnegans Wake.* Do you know why this sentence begins with a small letter?

40 In what twentieth century novel does the central character Philip Carey have a clubfoot? Can you also name the author?

41 Buck is kidnapped, sold, taken to the Klondike, beaten and brutalized. What is the novel, and who is the author?

42 What optimistic young lady, created by Eleanor Porter, was so capable of ignoring anything pessimistic that her name has come to mean that special kind of person?

43 What river is named in the title of an anthology by Edgar Lee Masters?

44 Who wrote plantation stories and beast fables containing Brer Rabbit and Brer Fox?

45 What is the temperature, according to science fiction writer Ray Bradbury, at which books will burn?

46 In what novel does Scout tell about her father's defense of a black man accused of raping a white woman?

47 What was the first typewritten book manuscript (1875) in America?

48 Below are characters in search of a book. See if you can match them.

Characters	Novel
1. Icabod Crane, Brom Bones	**(a)** *Portrait of a Lady*, Henry James
2. Ali Baba, Aladdin, Sinbad	**(b)** *Catch-22*, Joseph Heller
3. Yossarian	**(c)** *The Last Picture Show*, Larry McMurtry
4. Nick Adams	**(d)** *Women in Love*, D.H. Lawrence
5. Sonny, Duane, Jacy, Sam the Lion	**(e)** *Adam Bede*, George Eliot
6. Clyde Griffiths, Roberta Alden	**(f)** *An American Tragedy*, Theodore Dreiser
7. Isabel Archer, Lord Warburton	**(g)** *In Our Time* and *The Killers*, Ernest Hemingway
8. Hetty Sorrel, Dinah Morris	**(h)** *The Legend of Sleepy Hollow*, Washington Irving
9. Becky and Judge Thatcher	**(i)** *Arabian Nights, or One Thousand and One Nights*, anonymous
10. Gudrun, Gerald, Rupert, Ursula	**(j)** *David Copperfield*, Charles Dickens
11. Uriah Heep, Mr. Micawber	**(k)** *The Scarlet Letter*, Nathaniel Hawthorne
12. Hester Prynne, Roger Chillingworth	**(l)** *Tom Sawyer*, Mark Twain

49 Abraham Lincoln took this author by the hand and greeted her with: "Is this the little woman who made this great war?" Who was the little woman?

50 For a three-parter, name the character, the book, and the author of the following quotation, the last words of a famous American novel: "So we beat on, boats against the current, borne back ceaselessly into the past."

51 In what novel does Brother Juniper investigate the lives of five people killed in an accident to discover why God determined they should die?

52 The following writers have all won Pulitzer Prizes for fiction. Can you match the author to the work?

Author	Title
1. 1923 Willa Cather	**(a)** *A Summons to Memphis*
2. 1932 Pearl S. Buck	**(b)** *Breathing Lessons*
3. 1978 James Alan McPherson	**(c)** *The Color Purple*
4. 1980 Norman Mailer	**(d)** *Elbow Room*
5. 1983 Alice Walker	**(e)** *One of Ours*
6. 1984 William Kennedy	**(f)** *The Good Earth*
7. 1987 Peter Taylor	**(g)** *The Executioner's Song*
8. 1988 Toni Morrison	**(h)** *Beloved*
9. 1989 Anne Tyler	**(i)** *Ironweed*

53 Who wrote a book about a portrait that grows grotesque as the life of the artist who painted it grows more corrupt?

54 What novel begins with this scene: Dr. Bernard Rieux of Oran, a French port on the Algerian coast, sees a dead rat outside his door?

55 What is contradictory in the title of the novel *One Flew Over the Cuckoo's Nest*?

56 Who is the hero of the twenty-eight million books sold by the publisher of Mickey Spillane?

57 Memorable friendships have often been an important part of great works of fiction. See how well you can match the fictional friends that follow.

1. Robinson Crusoe and	**(a)** Orr
2. Don Quixote and	**(b)** Joe
3. Pantagruel and	**(c)** Sancho Panza
4. Huck and	**(d)** Melanie
5. Yossarian and	**(e)** Panurge
6. Scarlett and	**(f)** Friday
7. Pip and	**(g)** Jim
8. Charlotte and	**(h)** Stephen
9. Leopold Bloom and	**(i)** Tygger
10. Eyore and	**(j)** Wilbur

58 On what day is Bloomsday, when some Joyce mavens celebrate by reading *Ulysses* aloud from start to finish?

59 "Call me Ishmael" is the opening sentence of what novel?

60 What is the first American novel (published in 1859) known to be written by a black person? The book depicts hypocrisy among white abolitionists during the Civil War.

61 Here are some more characters in search of a novel. Can you help them?

Characters	**Novel**
1. Bernard Marx and the Ten World Controllers	**(a)** *As I Lay Dying*, William Faulkner
2. Natty Bumppo, Chingachook, and Hurry Harry	**(b)** *A Christmas Carol*, Charles Dickins
3. Jacob Morley and Mrs. Fezziwig	**(c)** *For Whom the Bell Tolls*, Ernest Hemingway
4. Robert Jordon, Pilar, and Maria	**(d)** *The Deerslayer*, James Fenimore Cooper
5. Cash, Darl, and Dewey Dell	**(e)** *Brave New World*, Aldous Huxley
6. Holden Caulfield and Phoebe	**(f)** *The Turn of the Screw*, Henry James
7. George, Lennie, and Curley	**(g)** *Tender is the Night*, F. Scott Fitzgerald

(Continued on the next page.)

Characters	Novel
8. Nichole and Dick Diver	**(h)** *Rabbit Run*, *Rabbit Redux*, and *Rabbit Is Rich*, John Updike
9. Eustacia Vye and Wildeve	**(k)** *Catcher in the Rye*, J.D. Salinger
10. Sonya, Natasha, and Pierre	**(l)** *Of Mice and Men*, John Steinbeck
11. Flora, Miles, and Peter Quint	**(m)** *The Return of the Native*, Thomas Hardy
12. Janice and Harry Angstrom	**(n)** *War and Peace*, Leo Tolstoy

62 From what book by James Hilton did we get the paradisical term Shangri-La?

63 "War is Peace, Freedom is Slavery, Ignorance is Strength." These were the mottos of the empire in which Winston Smith lived in a George Orwell novel. For a two-parter: (a) name the novel, and (b) name the empire.

64 Dashiell Hammett created a series of detective stories featuring a handsome, sophisticated couple and their dog. What were the names of these characters?

65 Ernest Hemingway said of this influential novel: "All modern American literature comes from one book by Mark Twain." What is the book?

66 What eighteenth century British author wrote *The Vicar of Wakefield*?

67 Literature is filled with lovers. Can you match the ones that follow?

1. Becky	**(a)** Don Quixote
2. Catherine	**(b)** Rhett
3. Dulcinea	**(c)** Tom Sawyer
4. Natasha	**(d)** Heathcliff
5. Scarlett	**(e)** Pierre
6. Jane	**(f)** Pip
7. Molly	**(g)** Mr. Darcy
8. Mattie	**(h)** Edward
9. Elizabeth	**(i)** Leopold
10. Estella	**(j)** Ethan

68 What beautiful fictional blonde of the Jazz Age had a "voice full of money"?

69 What is the full name of F. Scott Fitzgerald?

70 Which of Hemingway's novels was based on his own experiences as a reporter and Loyalist supporter in the Spanish Civil War?

71 What type of fish is caught by the old man in Hemingway's novella *The Old Man and the Sea*?

72 Santiago, the old man, and Manolin, the young boy, have a mutual hero, a sports figure, about whom they talk as they fish. Who is he?

73 What 1946 novel by Robert Penn Warren was based on the political career of Governor Huey Long of Louisiana?

74 What British novel published in three volumes in 1878 was set in Egdon Heath in Wessex, a setting that dominates the novel and suggests majesty and doom?

75 What eccentric French novelist, author of *Swann's Way*, worked in a cork-lined room?

76 "The street is Pyncheon Street; the house is the old Pyncheon House and an elm tree, of wide circumference rooted before the door, is familiar to every town-born child by the title of the Pyncheon Elm." By what more familiar name is this house on Pyncheon Street known to readers of the Nathaniel Hawthorne novel?

77 A Victorian novelist, admired by George Eliot and later Henry James, wrote *Mabel Vaughn*, *Mary Barton*, and *North and South*. She also wrote a biography of Charlotte Brontë. Who is this writer who was so much a part of her times that she refused to use her own first name?

78 These are the officers and crew of one of Her Majesty's fictional ships:

Lt. William Bligh, Captain; John Fryer, Master; Fletcher Christian, Master's Mate; Charles Churchill, Master-at-Arms; William Elphinstone, Master-at-Arm's Mate. Name the ship, the novel, and the authors.

79 What novel begins with this line: "It was the best of times, it was the worst of times, it was the age of wisdom, it was the age of foolishness . . ." and ends with this one: "It is a far, far better thing that I do, than I have ever done; it is a far, far better rest that I go to, than I have ever known"?

80 The author of *The Luck of Barry Lyndon* enjoyed using pseudonyms. For *The Paris Sketch Book* (1840) and *The Great Hoggarty Diamond* (1841), he used the name Michael Angelo Titmarsh. For *Confessions* (1842), he used the name George Savage Fitz-Boodle, an imaginary middle-aged clubman. Who is he?

81 A famous American author wrote science fiction for young people under the name Paul French. Who is he?

82 In what contemporary novel does a man named Henderson take a trip to Africa because a restless voice in his heart says, "I want, I want, I want"? For extra credit, who is the author?

83 All of these authors published a version of the same story: Tennyson,

Malory, John Cowper Powys, Charles Williams, E.A. Robinson, T.H. White. What was the story?

84 Badebec, the wife of Gargantua and mother of Pantagruel, died giving birth to Pantagruel—as well as to an assortment of other oddities including a train of mules, dromedaries, and camels laden with salted and smoked foods. Who wrote the outrageous novel in which these births occur, and what is the novel's name?

85 What novel by John Knowles, set at preppy Devon School, is a study of two sixteen-year-old boys reaching toward maturity and responsibility in the first months of World War II?

86 What is the job of Bartleby the Scrivner in Melville's long short story by that name?

87 Who was the French novelist and essayist, the companion of Jean Paul Sartre, who is best known for *The Second Sex*?

88 In what Dickens' novel does the interminable suit of *Jarndyce v. Jarndyce* form the background?

89 Who is the title character in a novel by Sinclair Lewis whose name has become a generic term for describing boring, un-

imaginative, middle-class businessmen, living insular small-town lives?

90 For this Matching Question, see how well you can pair the novels with the authors who wrote them.

Novel	Author
1. *Humphrey Clinker*	**(a)** Arthur Koestler
2. *The Trial*	**(b)** Max Beerbohm
3. *Darkness at Noon*	**(c)** Edward Everette Hale
4. *The Man Without a Country*	**(d)** Henry James
5. *Point Counter Point*	**(e)** Charles Dickens
6. *Portrait of a Lady*	**(f)** T.H. White
7. *Fathers and Sons*	**(g)** Franz Kafka
8. *Little Dorrit*	**(h)** Aldous Huxley
9. *Zuleika Dobson*	**(i)** Tobias Smollet
10. *The Once and Future King*	**(j)** Ivan Turgenev

91 What twentieth-century author wrote a series of short stories set in her native New Zealand? These include *Bliss, and other stories*, *The Garden Party*, *The Dove's Nest*, and *The Daughters of the Late Colonel.*

92 What Sinclair Lewis novel exposes the sexual hyprocrisy of a man of the cloth?

93 What 1962 work by South Rhodesian Doris Lessing, an experimental novel about a woman finding freedom from convention, was influential in the early Women's Movement?

94 What is the last name of the twentieth-century humorist who told stories in the language of baseball players, boxers, songwriters, chorus girls, stock brokers and the like? His first two names were Ringgold Wilmer.

95 Frank Stockton wrote a story in 1882 about a lady, her lover, her angry father, and two doors the lover must choose between to gain the hand of the lady. The lady was behind one door; what was behind the other?

96 What is the title of Boris Pasternak's epic novel about upheavals in twentieth century Russia?

97 What is the name of the fictional bridge that brought its author, Thornton Wilder, the Pulitzer Prize for fiction?

98 Who is the Polish-born American who writes novels (*Enemies: A Love Story*), short stories (*The Spinoza of Market Street*), and plays (*The Mirror*) in Yiddish?

99 This late nineteenth-century writer wrote stories dealing with scientific innovation and technology. His first published fiction was a short story called "Five Weeks in a Balloon," which appeared in 1863. What was his mas-

terpiece, written ten years later, and what was his name?

Answers

① The Princess of Cleves. *Mme. de LaFayette wrote four novels and, as was the custom of her day, denied knowledge of any of them. This novel details three social factions, each headed by a royal lady (one of them Catherine de Medicis, the king's wife), and the topic is* l'amour.

② The Tale of Genji. *Lady Murasaki's book, considered the oldest full novel in the world, was read and discussed by her contemporaries at the Imperial Court, where she was a servant to Empress Akiki, a girl of sixteen. A great work of Japanese literature, it has been compared to Marcel Proust's* Remembrance of Things Past *as a psychological study of decadent nobility.*

③ *The epistolary form, written as a series of letters.*

④ *Fielding wrote his novel as a parody of Richardson's* Pamela. Pamela*'s subtitle is* Virtue Rewarded, *which suggests why Fielding thought the book too moralistic. He created Joseph Andrews as a fictional brother of the unsufferably pure Pamela, and intended the work as parody. Instead, he created the English novel as we know it today: characters of some depth are outlined* *against their society by an author with an omniscient point of view.*

⑤ Tristam Shandy. *Still considered avant-garde literature because of its experimental form, even though it was written in the eighteenth century, it is the "autobiography" of one Tristam Shandy, gentleman, which begins before the author's birth, and is basically the story of the escapades of his Uncle Toby and the opinions of his father.*

⑥ *Six inches.*

⑦ War and Peace, *considered by many to be the greatest novel ever written.*

⑧ *We know the author as Stendhal. His other great work is* The Red and the Black *(1831).*

⑨ *Alyosha is the innocent brother, and Ivan is the skeptic.*

⑩ *Daniel Defoe, who also wrote* Robinson Crusoe *(1719).*

⑪ *Joseph Conrad, who is probably best known for the novel* Lord Jim *(1900).*

⑫ *Washington Irving. His* Sketch Book, *published in 1819–20, contained essays on English life and Americanized versions of European folk tales (e.g., "Rip Van Winkle" and "The Legend of Sleepy Hollow"). Irving signed his book under the pseudonym, Geoffrey Crayon.*

⑬ *Herman Hesse. The book, also called* Steppenwolf, *was published in 1924. Hesse, a German novelist and poet, won the Nobel Prize for Literature in 1946.*

⑭ *Robert Louis Stevenson.*

⑮ *His career as a river boat pilot on the Mississippi supplied Mark Twain with his pen name. In river pilot argot "Mark twain!" is the call for the depth of water of two fathoms.*

⑯ *Bret Harte. Probably his best known short story is "The Outcasts of Poker Flat."*

⑰ Treasure Island *by Robert Louis Stevenson.*

⑱ *Catch 22, which is also the title of the book by Joseph Heller.*

⑲ *Mr. Gant was a stone-cutter who made gravestones, some elaborately carved. The angel on the gravestone of Eugene Gant's dead brother, Ben, seems to lift its arm in salute to Eugene when he finally breaks free of his family and heads North to find his own identity.*

⑳ *Nathanael West is the author; the novel is* Miss Lonelyhearts.

㉑ *(a) They were boiled in oil. (They climbed into tall jars to hide, but were discovered and oil was poured on them.)*

㉒ *Anna Karenina, in a novel that bears her name, is a passionate Russian wife who takes a lover. After bringing her to vivid life, Tolstoy punishes Anna for rebelling against the norms of her society by having her fling herself under a train.*

㉓ *P.D. Wodehouse wrote* The Inimitable Jeeves *(1924),* Bertie Wooster Sees it Through *(1955), and* Much Obliged, Jeeves *(1971).*

㉔ *archy is the cockroach; mehitabel is the cat. (The two use no capital letters when typing their names.)*

㉕ *The novelists were F. Scott Fitzgerald and Ernest Hemingway.*

㉖ *The girl's name is Rosasharn, probably a mispronunciation of Rose of Sharon, a flowering bush. The novel is* The Grapes of Wrath *by John Steinbeck.*

㉗ *Hans Christian Andersen wrote these stories.*

㉘ *(a) The animal is a pig named Napoleon. (b) The novel, of course, is* Animal Farm, *(c) George Orwell's satire on Communism.*

㉙ *Sherwood Anderson (1876–1941), American short-story writer and novelist.*

(30) The Age of Innocence, *which won the 1921 Pulitzer Prize for fiction.*

(31) Gadsby *(1939).*

(32) *Some twenty people actually wrote this novel as a lark, each writing a chapter independently. Its publication under the name of Penelope Ashe was a hoax.*

(33) *The witty and inimitable Jane Austen, whose novel* Emma *(1816) is thought by some to be her greatest work.*

(34) *Thomas Mann.*

(35) David Copperfield.

(36) *William Faulkner wrote the sentence. The novel is* The Sound and the Fury.

(37) *F. Scott Fitzgerald.*

(38) *It was the first American novel to deal with lesbianism.*

(39) *The sentence begins with a small letter because it is the continuation of the final sentence of the 628-page book. The final sentence reads: "A way a lone a last a loved a long the" The structure and theme of the book is that of a cycle, so the first sentence completes the cycle begun in the last sentence.*

(40) *Philip Carey has a clubfoot in* Of Human Bondage *by W. Somerset*

Maugham. In this autobiographical novel, critics have said, the character's clubfoot substitutes for Maugham's own speech impediment, a stutter.

(41) The Call of the Wild *is the novel. Jack London wrote it. Buck, the main character, is a sled dog who winds up joining a pack of wolves.*

(42) *Pollyanna, the young lady who sees the best in the least promising situation in a novel of that name for young people.*

(43) *The Spoon River (a tributary of the Illinois) and its environs are the setting for the stories told in Masters'* Spoon River Anthology.

(44) *Joel Chandler Harris wrote* The Tales of Uncle Remus *from which these characters come.*

(45) *Fahrenheit 451, also the name of the novel by Bradbury, is a futuristic tale in which authorities demand that all books be burned.*

(46) To Kill a Mockingbird *(1960), Harper Lee's first and only novel, which won the 1961 Pulitzer Prize for fiction.*

(47) *Mark Twain's* The Adventures of Tom Sawyer *was the first. It was typed on a Remington Typewriter in 1875.* Life on the Mississippi *was also typewritten that same year.*

Twain did not publicize these facts because he did not want to give testimonials or to explain how to operate the machine.

(48) *1(h), 2(i), 3(b), 4(g), 5(c), 6(f), 7(a), 8(e), 9(l), 10(d), 11(j), 12(k).*

(49) *Harriet Beecher Stowe, author of* Uncle Tom's Cabin, *said to have incited the Civil War.*

(50) *The character is Nick Carraway; The book is* The Great Gatsby; *and the author is F. Scott Fitzgerald.*

(51) *Thornton Wilder's* The Bridge of San Luis Rey.

(52) *1(e), 2(f), 3(d), 4(g), 5(c), 6(i), 7(a), 8(h), 9(b).*

(53) *Oscar Wilde wrote* The Portrait of Dorian Gray.

(54) *This novel is* The Plague, *by Albert Camus.*

(55) *Cuckoos do not build nests; they lay their eggs in other birds' nests. The title of the book by Ken Kesey is irrational, befitting its subject, which is that of a perfectly sane man, R.P. McMurphy, tired of weeding peas on a penal farm, who commits himself to a mental institution where the inmates often seem more sane than the administrators. McMurphy "flew over" the nest of cuckoos, and changed it.*

(56) *Mike Hammer.*

(57) *1(f) Robinson Crusoe and Friday,* Robinson Crusoe*; 2(c) Don Quixote and Sancho Panza,* Don Quixote*; 3(e) Pantagruel and Panurge,* Gargantua and Pantagruel*; 4(g) Huck and Jim,* Huckleberry Finn*; 5(a) Yossarian and Orr,* Catch 22*; 6(d) Scarlett and Melanie,* Gone With the Wind*; 7(b) Pip and Joe,* Great Expectations*; 8(j) Charlotte and Wilbur,* Charlotte's Web*; 9(h) Leopold and Stephen,* Ulysses*; 10(i) Eyore and Tygger,* Winnie the Pooh.

(58) *June 16. This is the day on which Leopold Bloom set out to walk the streets of Dublin in James Joyce's* Ulysses.

(59) Moby Dick, *Herman Melville's masterpiece.*

(60) *The book is* Our Nig *by Harriet E. Wilson. It portrays, for the first time in American literature, a successful interracial marriage.*

(61) *1(e), 2(d), 3(b), 4(c), 5(a), 6(k), 7(l), 8(g), 9(m), 10(n), 11(f), 12(h).*

(62) Lost Horizon, *a novel concerning a man's spiritual quest that leads him to examine Eastern philosophies.*

(63) *(a)* 1984 *is the novel. (b) Oceania is the empire.*

(64) *Nick and Nora Charles, and their dog Asta.*

(65) Huckleberry Finn.

(66) *Oliver Goldsmith wrote this novel. A poet, essayist, and playwright, Goldsmith is probably best known for his comedy* She Stoops to Conquer, *first produced in Covent Garden in 1773.*

(67) *1(c) Becky and Tom Sawyer,* Tom Sawyer; *2(d) Catherine and Heathcliff,* Wuthering Heights; *3(a) Dulcinea and Don Quixote,* Don Quixote; *4(e) Natasha and Pierre,* War and Peace; *5(b) Scarlett and Rhett,* Gone With the Wind; *6(h) Jane and Edward,* Jane Eyre; *7(i) Molly and Leopold,* Ulysses; *8(j) Mattie and Ethan,* Ethan Frome; *9(g) Elizabeth and Mr. Darcy,* Pride and Prejudice; *10(f) Estella and Pip,* Great Expectations.

(68) *Daisy Buchanan in* The Great Gatsby *is described this way.*

(69) *Francis Scott Key Fitzgerald; he claimed to be related to the writer of the words to our national anthem.*

(70) *This Hemingway novel is* For Whom the Bell Tolls.

(71) *He caught a marlin.*

(72) *Joe DiMaggio.*

(73) All the King's Men. *Warren, who was born in Kentucky in 1905, is considered one of the best modern Southern writers.*

(74) The Return of the Native *by Thomas Hardy.*

(75) *Marcel Proust, author also of* Remembrance of Things Past, *was a man of such refined sensibilities that he claimed to be able to work only in this setting.*

(76) *We know this structure as* The House of Seven Gables.

(77) *Mrs. Gaskell (Elizabeth Cleghorn Stevenson Gaskell). She exposed some of the social horrors of the 1830s and 1840s in England. Married to a high-minded Unitarian minister William Gaskell, she wrote under the name Mrs. Gaskell. In* Mary Barton, *she wrote of the bleak lives of Manchester factory hands. Her* Life of Charlotte Brontë *(1857) is considered definitive.*

(78) *The* Bounty *in* Mutiny on the Bounty *by Charles Nordhoff and James Norman Hall.*

(79) *These lines open and close* A Tale of Two Cities *by Charles Dickens.*

(80) *William Makepeace Thackery, 1811–1863, who was best known for his novel* Vanity Fair. *He was a bit of a wit and a wag and enjoyed writing good-natured satire under various pseudonyms.*

(81) *Isaac Asimov.*

(82) Henderson, the Rain King *by Saul Bellow.*

(83) *All of these authors wrote a version of the King Arthur story.*

(84) *François Rabelaise, a French writer of the sixteenth century. The name of the novel is* Gargantua and Pantagruel.

(85) A Separate Peace.

(86) *In a law office on Wall Street, Bartleby's job was to copy and proofread legal documents, until he proclaimed that he "should prefer not to." He chose to starve instead.*

(87) *Simone deBeauvoire, writer, intellectual, and influential feminist.*

(88) Bleak House. *By the time the dispute is settled, all the money in disputation has been spent on lawyers.*

(89) *Babbitt, a character in Lewis' novel by that name.*

(90) *1(i), 2(g), 3(a), 4(c), 5(h), 6(d), 7(j), 8(e), 9(b), 10(f).*

(91) *Katherine Mansfield wrote short stories set in New Zealand.*

(92) Elmer Gantry.

(93) *This influential book is* The Golden Notebook.

(94) *Lardner.*

(95) *A tiger, in Stockton's story "The Lady or the Tiger."*

(96) Dr. Zhivago.

(97) *The bridge of San Luis Rey in the novel by that name.*

(98) *Nobel Laureate for Literature (1978), Isaac Bashevis Singer, who also writes charming sketches and children's stories.*

(99) *Jules Verne is the author. His masterpiece is* Around the World in Eighty Days.

Who Am I? Fictional Characters

In this chapter, fictional characters speak for themselves. See if you can guess who they are from the descriptions they give.

1. I am a villainous old man who trains young boys to pick pockets and steal for me.

2. I always say Yes Yes to life but I do so in a great many breathless and unpunctuated words

3. I am the gamekeeper at Wragby. I had a lovely romance that caused no end of trouble for Connie and me.

4. I was nicknamed Plain Buttons because I had no country. I was a prisoner on a ship, the *Nautilis*, for fifty years in a novel by Edward Everett Hale.

5. John Claggart lied about me because he was jealous, so the captain of the ship had me hanged. But I went to the gal-

lows shouting "God Bless Captain Vere!"

❻ I am Caroline Meeber in a book by Theodore Dreiser that was once considered scandalous. By what name do most people know me?

❼ You might not think much of my job, but I was proud to be the water carrier for a British regimen in India.

❽ I said this memorable line: "After all, tomorrow is another day."

❾ I was one of the *Little Women*—the one who married a professor and started a school for little men.

❿ In a 1924 novel, I am the anemic soul who spends some time in a tuberculosis sanatorium high on a mountain in Switzerland. I fell in love with another invalid, Claudia, and before she left for good we exchanged X-ray plates as mementos of our love.

⓫ I suffered a war wound that put me out of commission in bed. Brett, the woman I loved, wouldn't let me forget it and didn't like me to touch her, because it reminded her of my disability. But then Brett only wanted what she couldn't have.

⓬ I am the cuddly title character in children's stories by A. A. Milne.

13. Though I am a man, I have a dowager's hump. I am a bell ringer, and my name means "newborn babe."

14. I am so indecisive that I even have these questions in a poem named for me: "Shall I part my hair behind? Do I dare to eat a peach?" I also measure out my life in coffee spoons.

15. I awoke one morning from an uneasy dream and found myself transformed into a gigantic insect.

16. My first name is Joe. I was abandoned at an orphanage on Christmas Eve.

17. I am a professor of metaphysico-theologo-cosmolonigology in a novel by Voltaire. I believe that "all is for the best in this best of all possible worlds."

18. We are a group, in a novel by Johann Wyss, who are shipwrecked and live on a desert island for many years.

19. In a Nathaniel Hawthorne tale, my father is a scientist with a garden in which he cultivates plants for potents and medicines. He made a poison for me and my lover, Giovanni. Thereafter, everything that we breathed on was doomed to die. Whose daughter am I?

20. We all had a fine holiday, finally, and I said, "God bless us everyone."

21 I am the title character who narrates a famous Dickens' book. The first sentence of my story is this: "Whether I shall turn out to be the hero of my own life or whether that station will be held by anybody else, these pages must show."

22 I am the one-legged Captain of the *Pequod.* Admittedly, I am a bit obsessed with capturing a particular great white whale.

23 I was a king's jester, but I am now deceased. The prince, however, found my skull and said he remembered me—or words to that effect.

24 I was the feline who vanished, leaving only a smile, in a fantastic dream in which a rabbit ran down a hole.

25 All the perfumes of Arabia could not wash my hands clean.

26 In a poem by E.A. Robinson, I seem like an upperclass man to envious onlookers. They think I am "richer than a king," and "schooled in grace." But one night I went home and put a bullet through my head.

27 In Sir Walter Scott's *Ivanhoe*, I am a Saxon beauty, Queen of the Tournament. I am kidnapped and have many adventures, but at last I marry my love, Ivanhoe.

❷❽ Some say I am a selfish, shrewd, and ruthless young lady, and that *Vanity Fair* is a good place for me.

❷❾ I am a spinster. My cad of a lover jilted me on the eve of our wedding. But I'll show him: I'll just sit here in my tattered, yellowing wedding dress, while my wedding cake lies moldering on the table.

❸⓿ I may be ugly, but in one of Shakespeare's plays I can read the future. This is how I do it: "By the pricking of my thumbs, something wicked this way comes."

❸❶ I am well-known for this line: "Frankly, my dear, I don't give a damn."

❸❷ I am a young horse of a different color in a novella by John Steinbeck. I belong to 10-year-old Jody. This book contains a famous passage in which Billy Buck, the hired hand, delivers a foal by killing the mare.

❸❸ I am a rooster, very proud of my fine crowing. However, it nearly got me into hot water one time when I was carried off by a fox. I escaped him only by my shrewd wit.

❸❹ I am the bird-girl in *Green Mansions* who can commune with nature.

❸❺ James Thurber created me as an ordinary, boring man. But I have a secret life in which I am a hero.

36 I was a young girl with a lovely singing voice, but I was tone deaf. I fell under the spell of Svengali, however, and he helped me sing on pitch. But he was so cruel that I was glad when he died.

37 Some call me "The Knight of the Woeful Countenance." I saw a windmill and believed it to be a giant, so I attacked it. Unfortunately, I was wrong again and was nearly killed by this experience.

38 I am the sidekick of the knight in the previous question. I always come to his rescue when his impossible dreams get him into trouble.

39 I told the stories of *The Thousand and One Nights.*

40 I am a Russian student so destitute that I commit a murder to help my family eat. But I cannot bear the guilt.

41 I am a boy who never grew up. J.M. Barrie created me.

42 I am romantic, dashing, brave, and bold, but I have an enormous nose that rather puts the ladies off.

43 My man is called Watson, and I often tell him that solving crimes is elementary.

44 Our five lovely daughters are the central characters in *Pride and Prejudice.*

45 Though I was King Arthur's wife, I became mistress to Sir Lancelot. It did not turn out well.

46 In Shelley's dramatic poem (as in ancient Greek mythology) I struggled with Zeus about divine justice. I was cruelly punished. Aeschylus wrote a play about me, too.

47 I am a dangerous, brooding man in love with Catherine Earnshaw.

48 As a philosophy teacher and his student, we fell in love in medieval times. This was not appropriate. He became a monk, and I, a nun. We continued to love one another passionately.

49 After traveling into the dark continent and seeing monstrous acts, my dying words were, "The horror! The horror!"

50 In the *Paradiso,* I am Dante's guide through heaven.

51 I went off to fight the Trojan war, and while I was gone my wife took up with my cousin. When I returned, my faithless wife murdered me. Later, my son and daughter wreaked vengeance on their mother and her paramour.

52 My body lies a-moldering in the grave, but my soul is marching on. Stephen Vincent Benet wrote a poem about me.

53 I am the hideous dog that guards the gate to hell.

54 We are Chingachook and Uncas, the last surviving members of what Indian tribe?

55 I was a prisoner in a brutal Siberian camp. Alexander Solzhenitsyn wrote a story about one day in my life.

56 I am a kinsman of King Arthur. Some say I am his illegitimate son; some say I am his nephew. I hate the king so much that I help destroy his kingdom and the Round Table.

57 It is to pay their respect to me in Canterbury that Chaucer's pilgrims come, for I have been murdered in the cathedral by henchmen of King Henry II. T.S. Eliot wrote a narrative based on my life, but I was a real person, as well as one celebrated in fiction.

58 I grow from street urchin to lady in a 1914 play by George Bernard Shaw.

59 I am a priest-detective in a series of novels by G.K. Chesterton.

60 I was born in Newgate Prison, married five times (once to my brother), was a whore for twelve years, a thief for twelve more, and a transported felon in Virginia for eight. But at last I grew rich, lived honestly, and died a penitent.

61 I am the vanishing character in an unfinished 1870 novel by Charles Dickens. I was betrothed to Rosa Bud, but I mysteriously disappeared.

62 I am the fictional artist in *A Portrait of the Artist as a Young Man.*

63 My autobiography was begun before I was born, and it contains the adventures of my Uncle Toby and the opinions of my father.

64 I am a tall, brave, homely woman, relentlessly dedicated to the Republican cause in the Spanish Civil War. I initiated Robert Jordon into the ways of guerilla warfare.

65 I am a squire with a lovely daughter in *Tom Jones.* What is my family name, and who is my daughter?

66 I am the long-dead partner of Ebenezer Scrooge. My ghost visits him from time to time.

67 I am a member of the Reform Club in London, but I'm best known for a trip I took around the world.

68 My lover's friend was kind enough to say of me: "Age cannot wither her, nor custom stale/her infinite variety."

69 Beware, all you citizens of Oceania. I am watching you!

70 I am an honorable man. At least that is what is said of me in a famous speech—but I think the speaker had his tongue in his cheek.

71 I ran away from boarding school because society seemed corrupt to me. I had a dream about rescuing my young sister Phoebe as she ran through a grainfield.

72 I am the vicious and cruel overseer of slaves on a plantation in the South; however, I hail from New England.

73 I am a mischievous creature in a comedy by Shakespeare, and I don't think much of these people running around here in this forest. "Lord, what fools these mortals be!"

74 Our motto is "All for one and one for all" in a novel by Alexander Dumas.

75 I sold my soul to the devil in exchange for youth, knowledge, and power.

76 I am lying here in my bed about to expire, and I hear Cash outside my

window sawing the boards for my casket. This sounds terrifying, but I'll go through a lot worse before this family finally gets me buried in Jefferson.

Answers

① *The villain is Fagin in Charles Dickens'* Oliver Twist.

② *Molly Bloom is the yea-sayer in James Joyce's* Ulysses.

③ *Mellors, the game-keeper who was Constance's lover, in* Lady Chatterley's Lover *by D. H. Lawrence.*

④ *Philip Nolan in* The Man Without a Country.

⑤ *Billy Budd (considered a symbol of perfect purity) in Melville's novel of that name.*

⑥ *Sister Carrie in the novel of that name.*

⑦ *Gunga Din in Rudyard Kipling's poem of that name.*

⑧ *Scarlett O'Hara in* Gone With the Wind.

⑨ *Jo March in the novel* Little Women *by Louisa May Alcott.*

⑩ *Hans Castrop in Thomas Mann's* The Magic Mountain.

⑪ *Jake Barnes in Ernest Hemingway's* The Sun Also Rises.

⑫ *Winnie the Pooh.*

⑬ Quasimodo, *in Victor Hugo's novel* The Hunchback of Notre Dame.

⑭ *J. Alfred Prufrock in the poem by T.S. Eliot had trouble making up his mind.*

⑮ *Gregor Samsa in Kafka's* The Metamorphosis.

⑯ *Joe Christmas in Faulkner's* Light in August.

⑰ *Professor Pangloss in Voltaire's* Candide.

⑱ *This group is the Swiss Family Robinson.*

⑲ *Rappacinni's daughter (Beatrice) in a short story by that name.*

⑳ *Tiny Tim in* A Christmas Carol *by Dickens.*

㉑ *David Copperfield in Dickens' novel by that name.*

㉒ *Captain Ahab in Herman Melville's* Moby Dick.

(23) *Yorik. Hamlet found his skull and said: "Alas, poor Yorik. I knew him, Horatio."*

(24) *The Cheshire Cat in* Alice in Wonderland.

(25) *Lady Macbeth cannot get the stains of blood from her hands.*

(26) *Richard Cory in a short, shocking poem by this name.*

(27) *The fair Rowena.*

(28) *This sharp-tongued young lady is Becky Sharp.*

(29) *Miss Havisham in Dickens'* Great Expectations.

(30) *This is one of the three witches in* Macbeth.

(31) *Rhett Butler, in whom Scarlett O'Hara finally met her match, from Margaret Mitchell's 1936 novel about the Civil War,* Gone With the Wind.

(32) *The red pony in Steinbeck's work of that name.*

(33) *Chanticleer, the rooster, in* The Canterbury Tales.

(34) *Rima is the bird-girl.*

(35) *Walter Mitty in* The Secret Life of Walter Mitty.

(36) *Trilby in George du Maurier's novel of that name.*

(37) *Don Quixote in the Cervantes' novel of that name.*

(38) *Sancho Panza.*

(39) *Scheherazade told the stories to her husband, the king, a different tale every night for 1001 days. The collection of stories is sometimes called* The Thousand and One Nights *and sometimes* The Arabian Nights.

(40) *Raskolnikov in Dostoevsky's* Crime and Punishment.

(41) *Peter Pan.*

(42) *Cyrano de Bergerac in Edmund Rostand's play of that name.*

(43) *Sherlock Holmes, created by Sir Arthur Conan Doyle.*

(44) *Mr. and Mrs. Bennett.*

(45) *Guinevere.*

(46) *Prometheus. Aeschylus wrote the play* Prometheus Bound. *Shelley wrote the poem* Prometheus Unbound.

(47) *Heathcliff is the menacing lover in* Wuthering Heights.

(48) *Heloise is the student, and Abelard is the teacher.*

(49) *Mr. Kurtz in Joseph Conrad's* The Heart of Darkness.

(50) *Beatrice, Dante's symbol of the "eternal feminine."*

(51) *Agamemnon, in a play of that name by Aeschylus.*

(52) *The character is John Brown in "John Brown's Body."*

(53) *Cerberus in Greek mythology and later literature.*

(54) *The Mohicans in James Fenimore Cooper's* The Last of the Mohicans.

(55) *Ivan Denisovich in* One Day in the Life of Ivan Denisovich.

(56) *Modred.*

(57) *Thomas à Becket about whom King Henry II said in exasperation, "Will no one free me of this turbulent priest?" His barons, thinking he meant it, brutally murdered Becket in Canterbury Cathedral.*

(58) *Eliza Doolittle grew from waif to lady in* Pygmalion.

(59) *Father Brown.*

(60) *Moll Flanders in the Daniel Defoe novel by that name.*

(61) *Edwin Drood in the novel* The Mystery of Edwin Drood.

(62) *Stephen Dedalus.*

(63) *Tristram Shandy in the Laurence Sterne novel by that name.*

(64) *Pilar in Ernest Hemingway's novel* For Whom the Bell Tolls.

(65) *Squire Western. Sophia Western is the Squire's daughter.*

(66) *The ghost of Jacob Morley in* A Christmas Carol *visits Scrooge.*

(67) *Philias Fogg in Jules Verne's* Around the World in Eighty Days.

(68) *Enobarbus said this of Cleopatra in* Antony and Cleopatra.

(69) *Big Brother is watching you, and all of Oceania, in* 1984.

(70) *Brutus. Mark Antony said this, ironically, of Brutus in* Julius Caesar.

(71) *Holden Caulfield "catches" Phoebe in Salinger's* Catcher in the Rye.

(72) *Simon Legree in Harriet Beecher Stowe's novel* Uncle Tom's Cabin.

(73) *Puck says the quoted words in Shakespeare's* A Midsummer Night's Dream.

(74) *The Three Musketeers.*

(75) *Faust sold his soul to the devil in Goethe's* Faust.

(76) *Addie Bundren in Faulkner's* As I Lay Dying.

Who Am I? Famous Writers

TURN THE PAGE TO SEE WHO WE ARE

A. JAMES JOYCE
B. EDGAR ALLAN POE
C. ERICA JONG
D. MARK TWAIN
E. D. H. LAWRENCE
F. MAYA ANGELOU
G. ALEXANDER DUMAS
H. ANNE FRANK
I. AESOP (AFTER VELASQUEZ)
J. GERTRUDE STEIN
K. FYODOR DOSTOYEVSKY

It's time for the writers to have their say. Here, actual writers (either living or dead) ask us to identify them from the few clues they give. See how many you know.

❶ My autobiography is titled *I Know Why the Caged Bird Sings.*

❷ I am the author of *Franny and Zooey* and *Lift High the Roofbeam Carpenter.* I have not been heard from lately.

❸ I was a pediatrician in Rutherford, New Jersey, who wrote poetry between house calls. I became a distinguished American poet by writing imagistic poems about plums, iceboxes, wheelbarrows, white chickens, and other mundane subjects.

❹ I was the French writer who served twenty-seven years in prison for sex offenses.

5 I was a British Lord who wrote a series of letters to my son to instruct him in the ways to comport himself. A formal top-coat is named for me.

6 I was the wife of a famous writer, but I often felt neglected. I was also a writer, a dancer, and a painter. In effect, my husband and I named an era in the 1930s. I died tragically, trapped in a fire in a mental hospital in Ashville, North Carolina.

7 I wrote the first best-selling novel in America. It was printed in Philadelphia in two volumes in 1794. In a later English edition, the name of the novel was changed to *Charlotte Temple.*

8 My name usually evokes images of discipline, hard work, and success. I wrote about Ragged Dick who changed his name to Richard Hunter, Esq., when fame and fortune came his way.

9 I opened the first all-paperback book store and continued to run it while writing poetry and publishing City Lights Books. I wrote *Pictures of the Gone World*, and *A Coney Island of the Mind.*

10 I am an author of popular novels for young people. One of them is called *Are You There, God? It's Me, Margaret.*

⓫ I am Baronness Karen Blixen, Danish author of *Out of Africa* and other stories. By what name do you know me?

⓬ My name is Edward Stratemeyer, but I have several pseudonyms. One of them is that of a woman who wrote Nancy Drew mysteries. What is her name?

⓭ I was born in 1612 in Northampton, England. I wrote *The Tenth Muse Lately Sprung Up in America,* the first collection of verse produced in the new world. Twentieth century American poet, Adrienne Rich, said of me that I wrote "the first good poem in America, while rearing eight children, lying frequently sick, and keeping house at the edge of the wilderness."

⓮ I am the illegitimate son of the writer, Alexander père. I wrote *La Dame aux Camelias,* the basis for a famous Verdi opera.

⓯ I have written 465 books, and if I live and continue to work, I will probably reach 500 in late 1993. I have written books on God and robots, gods and martians, limericks and physics, space exploration, and children's literature. I am the most prolific writer in the world.

⓰ I wrote an expose of the Chicago stockyards called *The Jungle.* I also wrote *Oil!* Later, I was almost elected governor of California.

17 I wrote a novel called *Barren Ground.* When I traveled, as I often did, I wrote postcards home to my dogs, Mr. Jeremy Glasgow and Mr. Billy Bennett. (One of my dogs was named for me.)

18 I was the first important black poet in America. I was brought to Boston as a slave in the 1760s and took the last name of the family that bought me. I published my first poems at age 20.

19 I was a speech writer for Lyndon B. Johnson before writing the best seller *Jaws.*

20 I am a French aviator who wrote lyrical narratives about flying, but I am best known for a book for children, *The Little Prince.*

21 I am William S. Porter, an American writer famous for short stories with surprise endings. I began writing when I was convicted of embezzlement in Texas and had to spend three years in prison. You know me by my pen name.

22 I am a famous English mystery writer who created a suave Belgian detective, Hercule Poirot. I have also written several "straight" novels under the pen name of Mary Westmacott.

23 I am a poet, critic, and translator. During World War II, I broadcast fascist propaganda to the United States. I was indicted for treason and confined to a mental hospital.

24 In 1847, my novel, *Agnes Grey,* was published in England as a set along with the novel of my sister. Her novel was more popular, and she became more famous than I. Her name is Emily Jane. What is mine?

25 I was married to a famous Romantic poet who died when his boat capsized in 1822. Though he is thought to be the artist of the family, the terrifying character I originated in my 1818 novel is recognized by far more people than any of his.

26 In 1897 I created a ghoulish creature that—along with the terrifying monster in the preceding question—has come to be the quintessential fiend.

27 I wrote the popular adventure novel in which these were the major seagoing characters: Billy Bones, Jim Hawkins, Old Pew.

28 My real name was Amandine Aurore Lucile Dupin, Baronne Dudevant, and I really got around: I had love affairs with Prosper Merimee, Alfred De Musset, and Frederic Chopin—just to name a few. In between, I wrote books. Most people know me by my pen name.

29 I was a distinguished lepidopterist who became famous for creating a distinctive nymphet. I am also regarded as a brilliant stylist.

30 My real name is Arthur Sarsfield Ward, and I am best known for writing thirteen books about Fu Manchu, a Chinese genius and criminal. Do you know my pen name?

31 I wrote many creepy fictional works, but the most popular is still *Hound of the Baskervilles.*

32 I was born in Indian Creek, Texas, and was a great-grandniece of Daniel Boone and a cousin of O. Henry. I am considered among the masters of the short story—"Flowering Judas" is one I wrote.

33 I was born into a famous New England literary family, but I settled permanently in England in 1875. When I died, I directed that my ashes be taken to Mount Auburn Cemetery in Cambridge, Massachusetts. For extra credit, name my sister and my brother, as well.

34 I am the author of a fictionalized portrait of myself as a young man in Dublin.

35 I am the English poet known for dramatic monologues and for my correspondence with a certain Miss Barrett. I wrote

this famous line: "Ah, but a man's reach should exceed his grasp, or what's a heaven for?"

36 My popular adventure story, *Kim*, was set in India.

37 My subtle, ironic attacks on suburbia have often been published in *The New Yorker,* but I am best known for my best-selling novels *The Wapshot Chronicle* (1957) and *The Wapshot Scandal* (1964).

38 I am a contemporary Catholic priest well known for writing steamy novels.

39 In the seventeenth century, I was imprisoned and wrote "To Althea from Prison." I was released and later imprisoned again. This time I wrote "To Lucasta, Going to the Wars."

40 I am best known for my novel about a woman called Isadora Wing who overcame a great fear.

41 I wrote an epistolary novel with a vivid color in the title.

42 I wrote the following lines of poetry:

"I grieve and dare not show my discontent,
I love and yet am forced to seem to hate,
I do, yet dare not say I ever meant,
I seem stark mute but inwardly do prate."

And I also supervised naval raids against the Spanish Armada and defeated Philip II of Spain in 1588.

43 I am an English novelist buried in Taos, New Mexico.

44 I am probably best known for my poetry, but I also wrote a novel called *The Bell Jar.*

45 I am the Canadian who wrote *The Edible Woman, Lady Oracle,* and the chilling *Handmaid's Tale.*

46 A British poet, I celebrated the famous "death charge of the six hundred" at Balaclava in the Crimea, September 20, 1854, with these lines:

"Theirs not to make reply,
Theirs not to reason why,
Theirs but to do or die.
Into the valley of Death
Rode the six hundred."

47 My novel *To Kill a Mockingbird* was a bestseller, yet I never published another.

48 I am best known for another novel, but I am also the author of *Billy Budd.*

49 Environmentalists love my work. An American writer and scientist, I aroused controversy with my book *The Silent*

Spring (1962) in which I contend that indiscriminate use of insecticides are a hazard to wildlife and human beings.

50 At Charles Scribner's Sons I was the editor of the fiction of Thomas Wolfe, F. Scott Fitzgerald, Ernest Hemingway, Ring Lardner, and Taylor Caldwell. These people were a handful, I'll tell you.

51 I am one of the greatest novelists in the world. A Russian, I served four years of hard labor in a Siberian prison for associating with radical Utopians.

52 I am also a Russian writer, but I suffered from depression. Some called me a religious fanatic. I burned my novel *Dead Souls* and starved myself to death.

53 My real name is Eric Hugh Blair. In 1949 I wrote a novel that introduced several terms into the English language. Some of these were *doublethink*, *newspeak*, and *Big Brother*.

54 I created the character Tarzan and his friend Jane.

55 I am the French philosopher who became the leading exponent of twentieth century existentialism. I refused to accept the 1964 Nobel Prize in Literature because such awards make a writer too influential.

56 You know me as Jack, but my real name was Jean-Louis. I wrote the first American "road" novel.

57 I was born into a missionary family and reared in China. My experiences there are reflected in my novels *The Good Earth, Dragon Seed,* and others.

58 I wrote *The Yearling,* which won the Pulitzer Prize in 1938.

59 My books, called *The Leatherstocking Tales,* created the romance of the frontier in American literature.

60 I wrote devastating satires of American middle-class life, and I am the first American to win a Nobel Prize for literature.

61 I became John Milton's assistant as Latin secretary and entered Parliament in 1659.

62 I was born in Boston in 1809 to parents who were actors. They died when I was a child, and I was brought up by a Scottish couple (I took their name as one of my own). I attended the University of Virginia, and later went to West Point, but I lasted at the military academy for less than a year, being dismissed for neglect of duty. Later I married my invalid cousin, Virginia, who was then thirteen years old. Incidently, I wrote horror stories as well as poetry.

(63) Some took offense when I said that "the confusion of marriage with morality has done more to destroy the conscience of the human race than any other single error." Perhaps it was because I am British.

(64) I am an Anglican priest who proposed a rather interesting solution to my country's problems with overpopulation and food shortages.

(65) The first line of one of my novels is often quoted: "It is a truth universally acknowledged, that a single man in possession of a good fortune must be in want of a wife."

(66) William Dean Howells called me "the Lincoln of literature." My family in Missouri was not wealthy, but we did own land and a few slaves. One slave, Uncle Dan'l, was my friend when I was a boy, and I later based the character, Jim, on him.

(67) The hero of my novels is more famous than I am. He has become a household word, while most people do not know my name. If I said the word *Goldfinger,* you would know my hero. But what about me? Who am I?

(68) More than half of the books I wrote were set in Yoknapatawpha County.

(69) I am Charles Lutwidge Dodgson, and I wrote *The Hunting of the Snark,*

among other, better known stories. By what name do you know me?

70 I was a slave in the sixth century who told stories. One of them was "The Fox and the Grapes."

71 *The Brooklyn Times* reviewed my collection of poetry *Leaves of Grass.* The poet who reviewed it was extremely kind to the work. Who am I, and who was the reviewer?

72 Boz, as in *The Sketches of Boz,* was a pen name I used occasionally. I wrote many famous novels of social satire.

73 I wrote the novel *Deliverance,* and the screenplay. I was also an actor in the film.

74 I am the author of many poems and novels. My last novel was the tragic story of Jude Fawley, Arabella, Sue Bridehead, and "little Father Time."

75 Children still love my stories about Mowgli, the jungle boy brought up by Mother Wolf.

76 I wrote of *The Invisible Man,* who lived beneath the street.

77 We are brothers. Our first names are Jacob and Wilhelm. What is our last name, and what kind of fiction did we write?

78 The author of *The Heart is a Lonely Hunter* and other novels, I lived in Brooklyn Heights, New York, in the 1940s with possibly the most eclectic and electric group of artists of the twentieth century: W.H. Auden, Gypsy Rose Lee, Richard Wright, Benjamin Britten, Paul and Jane Bowles, and others.

79 I was a German-Jewish girl who hid from the Nazis in an Amsterdam building. I kept a journal during that time that was published after my death in a concentration camp.

80 My name was Mary Ann Evans. I wrote *The Mill on the Floss.* By what name do you know me?

81 I am a French novelist. I wrote about the "sentimental education" of one Frederic Moreau, a romantic young man who went to Paris from the provinces. My novel about a romantic young woman who stayed in the provinces is even more famous.

82 I based a very popular novel on the biblical story of Cain and Abel, but my characters, who lived in the Salinas Valley in California, were named Cal and Aron.

83 Although my name sounds and looks French, I was an English writer of popular novels that include *Rebecca, Frenchman's Creek,* and *My Cousin Rachel.*

84 Long before I wrote *The Caine Mutiny*, I was a comedy writer for Fred Allen.

85 I am the American writer responsible for the event called the Jumping Frog of Calaveras County Contest.

86 I wrote a series of books for children in which my own son is the only human character in a world of small animals.

87 I wrote *Advertisements for Myself*, but I didn't really need to advertise myself: I gained notoriety after I was accused of stabbing my wife. I also ran for mayor of New York City on the platform that the city should become a state.

88 I studied psychology at Radcliffe under William James and did lab experiments in brain anatomy at Johns Hopkins University. Later I set up housekeeping in Paris with a peculiar array of friends, acquired a dozen Picasso paintings, and wrote *Tender Buttons, Three Lives,* and *The Making of America.*

89 I wrote a novel (some considered it scandalous) about a prostitute. A bookbinder (some say mistakenly, some say deliberately) bound it into several hundred copies of the biography of John Wesley, founder of Methodism. Who am I, and what is the name of the novel?

90 My name means "Peace be with you," and it is on my sketches, including *Tevya's Daughters* that the play, *Fiddler on the Roof*, is based.

91 I am an American woman of the colonial period who established the first "literary club."

92 My friends were Lytton Strachey, Roger Fry, Bertrand Russell, and John Maynard Keyes. My sister was Vanessa Bell. We were all neighbors in London, where I lived with my husband Leonard.

93 I am the playwright of *The Children's Hour, The Little Foxes,* and *Watch on the Rhine.* My husband, mystery writer Dashiell Hammet, and I were black-listed during the McCarthy era. I wrote about this in *Scoundrel Time.*

94 Some call me America's most prolific woman novelist. And it is true that I publish a new book almost every year. My first was *Expensive People* in 1968. Others are *them, Wonderland, Bellefleur,* and *The Bloodsmoor Romance.*

95 I am a poet often associated with my friend, Sylvia Plath, for we were students together and were both "confessional poets." We were also young mothers who had difficulty making room in our lives for both our families and our art. And we died in similar ways.

96 William Wordsworth addressed me as his "dearest friend" in *The Prelude.* When I was twenty-four, I came to live with William at Grasmere, in the English Lake District. I began to keep journals to give William pleasure. I was upset when William decided to marry Mary Hutchison and bring her to live with us. However, I nursed his children and wrote verses for them.

97 I kept a famous diary that captured personal reactions to experience. My friends were Henry Miller and his wife June, with whom I lived for awhile, and the psychiatrist Otto Rank, who used my diary form as a technique to help his patients.

98 I am a Southern writer who often used violent means to get my vision across. My comic masterpiece is *Wise Blood,* in which I focus on a founder of "a church without Christ where the blind stay blind, the lame stay lame, and them that's dead stays that way."

99 I shocked many people with my 1963 novel, *The Group*, about sexual explorations of well-bred college girls. I was also a journalist and wrote about Vietnam and Watergate.

100 My novels include *Tar Baby*, *Sula*, and *Beloved.*

(101) I am the author of *Up the Down Staircase* and the daughter of Sholom Aleichem.

(102) The two of us—very different writers—won two Pulitzer Prizes for fiction each, a feat no other authors have accomplished. One of us won for *Alice Adams,* 1922; the other, for *The Reivers,* 1963.

(103) And I received the Pulitzer in 1950, not for *Alice Adams,* but for *Annie Allen.* Who am I?

Answers

(1) *Maya Angelou, a black writer and actress who frequently performs her own work on stage.* I Know Why the Caged Bird Sings, *her autobiography, begins with this line: "If growing up is painful for the Southern Black girl, being aware of her displacement is the rust on the razor that threatens the throat."*

(2) *J.D. Salinger. Salinger went into hiding after several early successes with novels such as these and* The Catcher in the Rye.

(3) *William Carlos Williams was the doctor/poet.*

(4) *The Marquis de Sade, from whom we get the word "sadist."*

⑤ *Lord Chesterfield, from whom the topcoat took its name, was a British statesman and author who lived from 1694 until 1773.*

⑥ *Zelda Sayers Fitzgerald lived a life of excess as wife of F. Scott Fitzgerald. Their names are connected with the Jazz Age. Never stable, Zelda spent time off and on in a mental institution. On March 10, 1948, she died, trapped in a fire on the top floor of the Ashville, North Carolina, mental hospital. Her body was identified by a charred slipper lying beneath it. Nancy Milford wrote* Zelda, *a best-selling biography of her, in 1970.*

⑦ *Susanna Haswell Rowson, an actress, wrote the first bestseller,* Charlotte, a Tale of Truth, *published in 1794. About two hundred editions of* Charlotte Temple *(the name to which it was changed) have been printed. Other works by Rowson are* Victoria *(1786),* The Inquisitor *(1788),* Rebecca, or the Fille de Chambre *(1792.)*

⑧ *Horatio Alger, who wrote one hundred popular books for boys. The moral of his novels was that any Tattered Tom, through hard work, can raise himself in the world. But good luck played not a little part in the "riches" side of Alger's "rags to riches" characters.*

⑨ *Lawrence Ferlinghetti, a poet who owned the City Lights bookshop in San Francisco in the 1960s.*

⑩ *Popular juvenile author Judy Blume. Blume has also written* Blubber, Deenie, Starring Sally J. Freedman As Herself, Then Again, Maybe I Won't, Tiger Eyes, *and many other novels for young readers.*

⑪ *Isak Dinesen. A Dane who wrote in English, Dinesen lived on a coffee plantation in Africa. She wrote her autobiography* Out of Africa *from these experiences.*

⑫ *Carolyn Keene. Stratemeyer had several other pseudonyms as well. Under one or the other he began these series of books:* The Rover Boys, Tom Swift, The Bobbsey Twins, The Dana Girls, *and* Hardy Boys. *His daughter, Harriet Stratemeyer Adams, took over the Stratemeyer Literary Syndicate after his death.*

⑬ *In 1650, Anne Dudley Bradstreet wrote* The Tenth Muse Lately Sprung Up in America. *The first collection of verse produced in the new world, it became one of the most popular books in seventeenth-century London.*

⑭ *Alexander Dumas. Alexander père (1802–1870) wrote* The Count of Monte Cristo *and* The Three Musketeers. *Alexander fils (1824–1895) wrote the play on which Verdi based* La Traviata.

⑮ *Isaac Asimov. No one has written more books than this author, who was born in 1920.*

⑯ *Upton Sinclair, who died in 1969, wrote the expose of the Chicago stockyards in 1906. A socialist, he captured the Democratic party in California in the 1930s and was almost elected governor.*

⑰ *Southern novelist Ellen Glasgow (1873?–1945) was eccentric (she made sure no one knows the exact year of her birth), but she cleared the ground for modern Southern literature. She had no formal education—her relatives taught her to read and write—but she won a Pulitzer Prize in 1942 for* In This Our Life.

⑱ *Phillis Wheatley, who was born in Africa in the early 1750s. This colonial poet wrote "Poems on Various Subjects, Religious and Moral," and identified herself as "Negro Servant to Mr. John Wheatley of Boston, in New England." (1773) She also wrote* Memoirs and Poems *(1834), and* The Letters of Phillis Wheatley, the Negro Slave-Poet of Boston *(1864).*

⑲ *Peter Benchley of the famous writing Benchley family. His father was Nathaniel Benchley, his grandfather, Robert Benchley.*

⑳ *Antoine Marie Roger Saint-Exupery, who also wrote* Wind, Sand, and Stars, *in 1939;* Night Freight, *in 1932; and* Southern Mail, *in 1929.*

(21) *William Sydney Porter was better known as O. Henry.* The Gift of the Magi *and* The Ransom of Red Chief *are among his three hundred stories. Porter worked as a teller in an Austin, Texas, bank in the 1890s, and later an unexplained shortage there was charged to him. Although many thought him innocent, he fled to Honduras, returning only to be with his dying wife. He was arrested and served three years in prison, where he began to write.*

(22) *Agatha Christie.*

(23) *Ezra Pound, born in Hailey, Idaho, in 1885. He was one of the most controversial and influential of twentieth-century poets. As an artist he was subtle and complex, but he was a political reactionary and was eventually indicted for treason. His most famous work is a cycle of poetry called* Cantos.

(24) *Anne Brontë. Her sister was, of course, Emily Brontë, whose book in the set was* Wuthering Heights. *Charlotte contributed a book to the set called* The Professor, *but the book was rejected by the publisher. (*Jane Eyre *was Charlotte's book published alone that same year.) The three sisters published at their own expense a book of their collected poetry under the pseudonym Currer, Ellis and Acton Bell (Charlotte, Emily, and Anne respectively) in 1846.*

㉕ *Mary Wollstonecraft Shelley (1797–1851) was an English writer who created the Frankenstein monster, in her 1818 novel. She was the second wife of poet Percy Bysshe Shelley.*

㉖ *Bram Stoker. Stoker created the title character of* Dracula.

㉗ *Robert Lewis Stevenson, who wrote* Treasure Island.

㉘ *George Sand took this name to hide her sex, but apparently she hid it none too well from some of the most famous male artists of her day. Sand wrote* Valentine *(1832),* Leila *(1833), and other novels.*

㉙ *Vladimir Nabokov, who became an international figure in 1955 after writing* Lolita, *a satire about a middle-aged European intellectual infatuated with a twelve-year-old American girl. The book became a modern American classic. Nabokov's work is erudite, witty, and dazzles with literary allusions and word games. Nabokov was also recognized as an international expert on butterflies, a lepidopterist.*

㉚ *Ward, a British mystery writer, used the pen name Sax Rohmer.*

㉛ *Sir Arthur Conan Doyle, known chiefly for his series of tales featuring master detective Sherlock Holmes and his companion, Dr. Watson.*

(32) *Katherine Anne Porter (1890–1980). Her books of stories include* Flowering Judas, Pale Horse, Pale Rider, *and* The Leaning Tower. *Her first novel,* Ship of Fools *(1962), set aboard a German ship shortly before Hitler came to power, is a moral allegory that attempts to recreate the atmosphere of a world on the brink of disaster.*

(33) *Henry James (1843–1916) adopted British citizenship in 1915 after he found life in America "provincial and uninteresting." He died a year later, and as he had directed, his ashes were brought back to Cambridge. His ambivalence about his citizenship can be seen in his work: James contrasts the sophisticated, staid Europeans with the innocent, brash Americans in his novels* Roderick Hudson, Daisy Miller, The Americans, Portrait of a Lady, *and* The Ambassadors. *His sister was Alice James, an overlooked writer and intellectual; his brother was William James, an American philosopher.*

(34) *James Joyce wrote* A Portrait of the Artist as a Young Man, *a thinly disguised autobiography.*

(35) *Robert Browning, whose romantic correspondence with Elizabeth Barrett resulted in their marriage and long love affair.*

(36) *Rudyard Kipling (1865–1936), an Englishman born in India. He wrote of Anglo-Indian life. A romantic imperalist, his attitude is reflected in his poems "The White Man's Burden," "Loot," "Mandalay," "Gunga Din," and* Recessional. *He married an American, lived in Vermont for four years, and wrote many children's stories, including* The Jungle Book, *while living there.*

(37) *John Cheever wrote about life in the affluent American suburbs. A comic/moralist, he found disintegration and evil in the world of barbeque grills and martinis.*

(38) *Father Andrew Greeley, ordained as a Catholic priest in 1954, insists he is a parish priest first, a writer second. Accused of writing "steamy" novels, he insists that his are theological novels in which the characters are on a quest for God, and human passions are but a hint of divine passion. The priest/storyteller/sociologist has written more than 110 books, including the nonfiction* The Church and the Suburbs, Angry Catholic Women, *and* Confessions of a Parish Priest; *and fiction,* The Cardinal Sins, Patience of a Saint, Angel First, *and* Love Songs.

(39) *Richard Lovelace (1618–1657?) was a Cavalier Poet. A Royalist, he was briefly imprisoned for having presented to Parliament a petition for the restoration of the bishops.*

He was released and later imprisoned in the Tower of London for his Royalist sympathies. He is best known for his two graceful lyrics, one to Althea, another to Lucasta.

(40) *Erica Jong wrote* Fear of Flying, *in which the heroine meditates on women "who are really free," such as Emily Dickenson, the Brontës, Virginia Woolf, Carson McCullers, and Sylvia Plath, and decides that "women are timid in their lives and brave only in their art." Jong has written a number of volumes of poetry and other books, including* How to Save Your Own Life.

(41) *Alice Walker, who wrote* The Color Purple, *was born in 1944 to Georgia sharecroppers. She is editor of the anthology of the writings of Zora Neale Hurston, has written essays, including* In Search of Our Mothers' Gardens, *and won the National Book award for* The Color Purple, *a novel that analyzes the effect of racism on black men and celebrates the resiliency of black women.*

(42) *The writer of "On Monsieur's Departure," a fragment of which is quoted here, is none other than Queen Elizabeth I (1533–1603). She was proficient in Greek, Latin, Italian, Spanish, French, and German. During her forty-five-year reign she wrote translations, speeches, and poems that revealed extraordinary wit and intelligence.*

(43) *D.H. Lawrence, a major figure in modern literature, traveled continually, looking for a homeland and congenial colleagues. At one time or another, he lived in Italy, Germany, Ceylon, Australia, New Zealand, Tahiti, the French Riviera, Mexico, and the southwest part of the United States. He settled in Taos, New Mexico, near Sante Fe, surrounded by admiring disciples, mostly women, and died there in 1930.*

(44) *Sylvia Plath wrote this novel about her life as a college girl and young magazine writer in New York. Later married to poet Ted Hughes, Plath could never find a way of comfortably combining her life as an artist with her role as a wife and mother. She took her own life (by gassing herself in the kitchen) after leaving cups of milk by the cribs of her two babies.*

(45) *Margaret Attwood was born in 1939 in Ontario, Canada. She writes of cultural survivors and especially of women who can survive their alien culture. She has written several volumes of poetry and has retold Homer's* Ulysses *from the silenced perspective of Ulysses' wife who was seduced and abandoned.*

(46) *Alfred, Lord Tennyson in "The Charge of the Light Brigade."*

(47) *Harper Lee. Born in 1926 in Monroeville, Alabama, Lee received a Pulitzer Prize in 1961 for* To Kill a Mockingbird, *a*

novel about a lawyer who defends a black man prosecuted on rape charges. Convicted and sent to prison, he escapes and is shot to death. The author compares this to the shooting of innocent songbirds by hunters. She has published nothing since.

(48) *Herman Melville (1819–1891) is a major figure in world literature. His classic work is* Moby Dick, *about a whaling captain's obsessive voyage to find the white whale that had ripped off his leg. The novel is a sea story, a dictionary of whales and whaling, a sociological critique of American class and racial prejudices, and a philosophical enquiry into the nature of good and evil.* Billy Budd *is the story of the sacrifice of an innocent.*

(49) *Rachel Carson (1907–1964) was an American writer and marine biologist who wrote books on the sea.* The Silent Spring *was her provocative study of the dangers of insecticides.*

(50) *Maxwell Perkins, perhaps the greatest American editor of fiction.*

(51) *Fyodor Dostoyevsky (1821–1881) is a towering figure in world literature. When young, he joined a group of radical Utopians who had an illegal printing press. He was arrested and sentenced to four years in Siberia. An epileptic, he endured great suffering there. His greatest work is* The Brothers Karamazov.

(52) *Nikolai Gogol (1809–1852) is called the father of Russian realism. His picaresque novel* Dead Souls *(1842) concerns the rogue Chichikov who buys the names of dead serfs from landowners to mortgage them as property. Haunted by moral and religious questions and unable to write a sequel to* Dead Souls, *Gogol burned his manuscript and fasted until he died.*

(53) *George Orwell introduced these terms in his novel* 1984. *Born in India, the British novelist and essayist wrote of the socio-political conditions of his time and the problem of human freedom.*

(54) *Edgar Rice Burroughs (1875–1950) wrote* Tarzan of the Apes *in 1914. He wrote other jungle and science fiction thrillers as well.*

(55) *John Paul Sartre, an individualist, was the leading spokesman for existentialism.*

(56) *Jack Kerouac's* On the Road *influenced a generation of writers. He also wrote* Dharma Bums, The Subterraneans, *and* Big Sur.

(57) *Pearl S. Buck (1892–1973) won the Nobel prize in literature in 1938 for* The Good Earth. *She wrote eighty-five books including those for children, a biography of her missionary parents, plays, nonfiction, and an autobiography.*

(58) *Marjorie Kinnan Rawlings (1896–1953) wrote* The Yearling, *which won her a Pulitzer. A newspaper reporter and writer, she settled in Cross Creek in north-central Florida and began writing on pastoral themes.*

(59) *James Fenimore Cooper (1789–1851) wrote* The Leatherstocking Tales *that featured frontiersman Natty Bumppo, nicknamed Leatherstocking. The novels detail the clash between frontier wilderness and encroaching civilization. The series includes* The Pioneers, The Last of the Mohicans, The Prairie, The Pathfinder, and The Deerslayer. *Cooper also wrote adventures on the high seas.*

(60) *Sinclair Lewis (1885–1951), author of* Main Street, Babbitt, Arrowsmith *(which won the Pulitzer), and* Elmer Gantry, *was a great satirist. Lewis refused the Pulitzer Prize because he thought the rules that Joseph Pulitzer had laid down were restrictive to writers and censored certain imaginative works.*

(61) *Christopher Marlowe (1564–1593). Arguably the greatest English dramatist before Shakespeare, Marlowe introduced blank verse in drama. His works include* Tamerlaine the Great, Dr. Faustus, The Jew of Malta, Edward II, *and a long poem,* Hero and Leander. *Marlowe was also a government agent, and some say it was for this reason that he was killed in a barroom brawl.*

(62) *Edgar Allan Poe, author of* The Fall of the House of Usher *and many more stories.*

(63) *George Bernard Shaw, considered the greatest British dramatist after Shakespeare. By introducing his drama of ideas, he revolutionized the Victorian stage that was dominated by melodramas. Shaw was married, but he had some biting comments about the state—as he had about most everything.*

(64) *Irish satirist and Anglican priest, Jonathan Swift, in* A Modest Proposal. *Swift's tongue-in-cheek solution was to kill the babies and then eat them.*

(65) *Jane Austen. This is the famous beginning of her novel* Pride and Prejudice.

(66) *Mark Twain, unsurpassed as humorist and social observer.*

(67) *Ian Fleming, creator of James Bond, Secret Agent 007.*

(68) *William Faulkner. Faulkner's works, mostly set in the South, include the novels* The Sound and the Fury *(1929) and* As I Lay Dying *(1930). Faulkner won the Nobel Prize for Literature in 1950.*

(69) *Lewis Carroll.*

(70) *Aesop. According to Herodotus, Aesop was a slave in Samos in the sixth*

century B.C. *Eventually, he was freed. His fables have been preserved through Babrius, Phaedrus, and Planudes Maximus. The most famous are "The Fox and the Grapes" and "The Tortoise and the Hare."*

⑺ *Walt Whitman, who reviewed the collection himself.*

⑻ *Charles Dickens.*

⑼ *James Dickey, Southern poet, novelist and teacher, wrote both the novel and the screenplay for* Deliverance. *For the inauguration of President Jimmy Carter in 1977, Dickey wrote and recited his poem "The Strength of the Fields."*

(74) *Thomas Hardy's last novel was the tragic* Jude the Obscure.

(75) *Rudyard Kipling. Kipling's most well-known children's stories are* The Jungle Book *(1894) and* Captains Courageous *(1897).*

(76) *Ralph Ellison's reputation is based on a single novel,* The Invisible Man, *a 1952 classic of American literature. For many years he taught English at New York University.*

(77) *Grimm. They are the Brothers Grimm who wrote grim fairy tales.*

(78) *Carson McCullers (1917–1967), author also of* Reflections in a Golden Eye, The Member of the Wedding, The Ballad of the Sad Cafe, *and the Broadway play* The

Square Root of Wonderful, *was an eccentric Southerner who lived a Bohemian life in New York City in the 1940s.*

(79) *Anne Frank, whose diary was published after World War II as* The Diary of a Young Girl. *The book was later dramatized as* The Diary of Anne Frank.

(80) *Mary Ann Evans is the nom de plume of nineteenth-century English novelist George Eliot. She also wrote* Middlemarch *(1872) and* Silas Marner *(1861).*

(81) *Gustav Flaubert, who also wrote* Madam Bovary.

(82) *John Steinbeck based* East of Eden *on this Biblical story.*

(83) *Daphne du Maurier. She wrote several popular romantic novels tinged with adventure or mystery.*

(84) *Herman Wouk, who also wrote* Winds of War.

(85) *Mark Twain. In addition to his better-known work, Twain wrote the comic masterpiece "The Celebrated Jumping Frog of Calaveras County," published in 1865 in the* New York Saturday Press.

(86) *A.A. Milne wrote the Pooh stories. Christopher Robin was modeled after his own son.*

(87) *Norman Mailer, American novelist, essayist, and journalist, who frequently shows himself as a bitter critic of American society.*

(88) *Gertrude Stein. Stein is credited with introducing the phrase "Lost Generation."*

(89) *John O'Hara is the author.* Butterfield 8 *is the novel.*

(90) *A leading figure in Yiddish literature, Sholom Aleichem (1859–1916) (which means "Peace be with you"), wrote* Tevya's Daughters, The Adventures of Mottel, the Cantor's Son, *and other sketches on which the popular 1964 Broadway musical* Fiddler on the Roof *was based. Aleichem's real name was Solomon Rabinowitz.*

(91) *Anne Hutchinson organized groups of women who met in her house as she led them in secular and theological discussions based on the literature of the day.*

(92) *Virginia Woolf. Woolf was a twentieth-century English writer whose best known novels are* Mrs. Dalloway *(1925) and* To the Lighthouse. *In 1941 she took her own life by drowning.*

(93) *Lillian Hellman (1907–1984). Her memoirs,* An Unfinished Woman, *won the National Book Award.*

(94) *Joyce Carol Oates says that she writes of her characters as a "psychologist of the human soul caught in the stampede of time." She has produced novels, short stories, collections of essays and poems. Astonishingly prolific, Oates writes novels that are often both popular and critically praised.*

(95) *Anne Sexton (1928–1974). A troubled child, adolescent and young woman, often under psychiatric care, she dropped out of college but remained a student of writing workshops until her death. Her book of poems,* Live or Die, *won a Pulitzer Prize in 1966. She wrote* The Death Notebooks *in 1974, shortly before she gassed herself in her garage.*

(96) *Dorothy Wordsworth (1771–1855). She adored her brother William and lived with him from 1795 until her death. She cared for him, kept lively, scrupulous journals recording their rural literary world, and fell into unrequited love with his friend Samuel Taylor Coleridge. After she became ill, Wordsworth played devoted nurse to her for the next twenty years in the house they continued to share.*

(97) *Anaïs Nin (1903–1977). Besides her* Diary, *Nin wrote a critical book,* The Novel of the Future, *in 1968. She reworked much of her diary experience in a series of novels*

that extended her exploration into the female psyche. The best-known is A Spy in the House of Love.

(98) *Flannery O'Connor (1925–1964) used grotesque humor, and often rural dialect, in her fiction. She suffered from lupus and died at age thirty-nine, but left* Wise Blood *and* The Violent Bear It Away, *as well as a collection of stories,* A Good Man is Hard to Find. Everything that Rises Must Converge, *a collection, was published posthumously.*

(99) *Mary McCarthy also wrote* Memories of a Catholic Girlhood *(1957) and* A Charmed Life *(1955).*

(100) *Toni Morrison, born in 1931 in Lorain, Ohio, is a teacher, book editor and novelist. Other novels include* The Bluest Eye *and* Song of Solomon.

(101) *Bel Kaufman, New York City teacher and writer.*

(102) *Booth Tarkington and William Faulkner. Both won two Pulitzers. Tarkington won in 1919 for* The Magnificent Ambersons *and in 1922 for* Alice Adams. *Faulkner won in 1955 for* A Fable, *and in 1963 for* The Reivers.

(103) *Gwendolyn Brooks.*

Copy Cat Quotes

Once a writer has come up with an apt phrase, others who come after tend to borrow the quotation for their own purposes. The appropriate use of another author's phrase or idea reinforces the original theme or image, and the constant repetition throughout generations of literature enriches these images and stamps them on our minds. This "borrowing," then, keeps literature alive and changing, as it builds on the old. Alluding to a familiar character, theme, title, or group of words already in our literature is also a shortcut for a writer, for he or she can call up with a word or a phrase—"the prodigal son," for example, or "Romeo and Juliet"—human themes that have echoed through the halls of time, but are still fresh today.

Below are a number of ideas, words, or themes that have been borrowed, and sometimes lent again. Can you identify the originators or the borrowers here?

1 A novel by Ben Ames Williams in the 1940s was about a woman so complicated it was impossible to judge her on earth. The name of the book was *Leave Her to Heaven*. This title was chosen from a passage in Shakespeare. Who said it? Was it (a) Banquo's ghost to Macbeth, (b) the ghost of Hamlet's father to Hamlet, or (c) one of the three witches?

2 American dramatist Marc Connelly wrote a play called *Green Pastures* in the early 1930s. From what earlier text did he take these words: (a) The Lord's Prayer, (b) The 23rd Psalm, or (c) The Apostle's Creed.

3 *Vanity Fair* is the title of a novel written by William Makepeace Thackeray in 1848. From whom was this title stolen, and what does it describe: (a) John Bunyan/a town fair, (b) Francis Beaumont/a club of egoists, or (c) Charles Beaudelaire/a box of jewels?

❹ Cervantes, in *Don Quixote*, used the phrase "to have and have not." What American novelist borrowed it for the title of a book?

❺ In his poem, "Under Ben Bulben," W.B. Yeats ends with these lines: "Cast a cold eye/On life, on death/Horseman, pass by!" An American novelist used the last three words as the title for his book about a young boy growing up in Texas among ranchers. (The book was later made into a film called "Hud.") Was it (a) Wallace Stegner, (b) Larry McMurtry, or (c) Larry L. King.

❻ The title of a 1939 novel was inspired by a passage from Revelations. In the passage, St. John the Divine has a vision of The Day of Judgment in which an angel says that the wicked will drink wine pressed from the grapes of God's anger. What is the name of the book, and who is the author?

❼ John Gunther, an American writer, titled a book *Death Be Not Proud*. Who originally used those words and in what work?

❽ A popular novel published in 1954 was called *Lord of the Flies*. Who wrote this novel, and to what earlier work does the title refer? (a) William Goldman/a history of war lords, (b) Charles Darwin/an essay on insects, or (c) William Golding/a Biblical story.

9 In T.S. Eliot's poem, "The Hollow Men," he uses the expression, "Mr. Kurtz, he dead." In what earlier novel do we find these words, and who wrote the novel?

10 A popular film in the fifties, starring Natalie Wood, was titled *Splendor in the Grass*. These words were borrowed from a British Romantic poet. Can you name him?

11 From which book of the Bible did Hemingway get the title of his 1926 novel *The Sun Also Rises*?

12 Contemporary American writer Gary Wills wrote a book of political satire called *Nixon Agonistes*. Earlier, T.S. Eliot had written a satire called *Sweeney Agonistes*. Someone before them had paired the word "Agonistes" with a famous biblical name. Was it (a) John Milton, (b) John Donne, or (c) Samuel Johnson?

13 In "Ode to a Nightingale," poet John Keats used the words "tender is the night." What twentieth century author used them later for the title of a novel?

14 In 1929 American novelist William Faulkner wrote a novel set in the South called *The Sound and the Fury*. From what other writer named William did he steal these words? (a) William Wordsworth, (b) William Shakespeare, or (c) William Congreve.

15 Lorraine Hansberry wrote a drama for the stage called *A Raisin in the Sun*. Her title paraphrases a poem by Langston Hughes. What was the name of the poem, and what was the line she paraphrased?

16 A popular scene transition in hokey Western films is described in these words: "meanwhile, back at the ranch." Shakespeare used a similar scene shift in words that appear in the stage directions to a number of his plays. These words were also borrowed for a later novel and film. Are these words: (a) waiting in the wings, (b) another part of the forest, or (c) Enter: Will Kemp?

17 In fifteenth century Florence, a fanatic Dominican friar named Savonarola confiscated books, paintings, dice, mirrors, lip rouges, perfumes and other items, and burned them in a raging fire in a public piazza. This fire was the inspiration for the title of a popular American book in the twentieth century. Can you identify the book and the author? Is it (a) *The Fire Next Time*/James Baldwin, (b) *The Bonfire of the Vanities*/Tom Wolfe, or (c) *Fire in the Lake*/ Frances Fitzgerald?

18 Humorist Nora Ephron wrote a book called *Crazy Salad*, which suggests that women often choose men to marry who are not appropriate for them. This term was first used in a similar way, referring to Venus, goddess of beauty, who chose the ugly, deformed Vulcan for a husband. ("It's certain that fine women eat/ A crazy salad with their meat.") The lines occur in the poem "A Prayer for My Daughter." Who wrote the poem? Was it (a) William Wordsworth, (b) W.B. Yeats, or (c) John Keats?

19 In a passage in *The Tempest*, Shakespeare uses the words "brave new world." Who later used this as the title for his satire aimed at utopians and advocates of a planned society?

20 Hemingway took his title *For Whom the Bell Tolls* from this passage by a metaphysical poet: "And therefore never send to know for whom the bell tolls; it tolls for thee." Is the first line of this "meditation": (a) "Bell, book, and candle," (b) "No man is an island," or (c) "Now tolls the knell of parting day"? For extra credit, name the poet who wrote the lines.

21 In John Bunyan's *Pilgrim's Progress*, Beulah land is a place of heavenly joy where the pilgrims rest until they are summoned to enter paradise. On what earlier work does Bunyan draw for his use of Beulah land: (a) *The Canterbury Tales*, (b) the Book of Isaiah, or (c) Dante's *Il Purgatorio*?

22 Eugene O'Neill wrote a play called *Mourning Becomes Electra*. The character, Electra, is an allusion to a mythological character, and the events in the myth have their counterparts in O'Neill's play. Was Electra (a) the mother of Oedipus, (b) the wife of Orestes, or (c) the daughter of Agamemnon?

23 Robert Penn Warren wrote a novel in 1950 titled *World Enough and Time*. To what earlier writer does he owe this title?

24 A Biblical story concerning King David tells of David's third son, Absalom, whom David loved. Absalom betrays his father and usurps his throne. When David's soldiers kill Absalom, David cries out in grief: "O my son Absalom! My son, my son Absalom! Would God I had died for thee. O Absalom, my son, my son." A twentieth-century American novelist takes the son's name for the title of a book and the theme of the Bible story for the book's theme. Who is this novelist and what is the exact title of the novel?

25 In 1942 Thornton Wilder wrote a play called *The Skin of Our Teeth*. Did he take this title from a passage in (a) *A Midsummer Night's Dream*, (b) The Book of Job, or (c) *Paradise Lost*?

26 Arthur Miller's play *After the Fall* is based on his life with actress Marilyn Monroe. To what "fall" was he alluding?

27 In 1494 a satirist named Sebastian Brant wrote *Narrenschiff*, a story about a ship that sailed the seas with a crew of selfish, foolish people, who carried with them all the vices and corruptions known to humankind. In 1509 a monk, Alexander Barclay, wrote *The Shyp o Folys of the Worlde*. In the 1960s an American writer used this same theme for a novel. For a two-parter: (a) what is the title of the novel written in the sixties and (b) who wrote it?

28 James Herriott, a veterinarian, wrote a book called *All Creatures Great and Small*. The title is from a poem by Coleridge. After a curse has been lifted in the poem, the central character blesses even "the little fishes" and says that God will not hear the prayers of man if man does not love all the creatures God made: "He prayeth best, who loveth best/All things both great and small." From which of Coleridge's poems did these lines and Herriott's title come?

29 In the late sixties Joan Didion wrote an essay called "Slouching to Bethlehem." The first person to use these words was William Butler Yeats in his poem "The Second Coming." On what original source did Yeats base his title: (a) The Book of Revelation (b) The Book of Kells or (c) The Book of Common Prayer?

30 A novel by Peter S. Beagle bears the title *A Fine and Private Place.* This line comes from an early British poet. Is it (a) Christopher Marlowe, (b) Andrew Marvell, or (c) Richard Lovelace?

31 In various versions of the legends of King Arthur, Sir Lancelot goes in search of the Holy Grail. What is a grail, and to what biblical story does the Holy Grail allude?

32 *Ars Poetrica*, a poem by Archibald MacLeish, relied on the work of a classical scholar for its title. Who wrote the earlier work?

33 Contemporary writer Ken Kesey wrote a novel titled *One Flew Over the Cuckoo's Nest.* Can you repeat the four-line children's folk rhyme from which he took his title?

34 From what writer did novelist Joyce Carol Oates take her title *Wonderland*?

35 The title of John Steinbeck's novel *The Winter of Our Discontent* came from a work by an English playwright. Can you name the English dramatist who used this phrase in an historical play?

36 Sigmund Freud asked, "What Does a Woman Want?" He was, perhaps unwittingly, paraphrasing the question of a certain pilgrim on the road to Canterbury in Chaucer's famous tale. Who was the person who repeatedly asked, "What does a woman like best?" For extra credit what was the answer?

37 Walker Percy wrote a novel titled *Love Among the Ruins.* From what English poet who received many love letters did he take his title?

38 Katherine Anne Porter took the title of her novel *Pale Horse, Pale Rider* from a Biblical passage that concerned the Four Horsemen of the Apocalypse. Was this passage in (a) Ecclesiastes, (b) Revelations, or (c) Isaiah?

39 The title of John O'Hara's novel *Rage to Live* came from an earlier work called *Moral Essays.* Who wrote the earlier work: (a) Alexander Pope, (b) John Lyly, or (c) Sir Thomas Browne?

40 Phrases used too often become cliches, but they were once fresh and precise. Here are some over-used phrases. Who said each of these first?

(a) Survival of the fittest: (1) Charles Darwin, (2) Herbert Spencer, or (3) Aldous Huxley?

(b) Take it with a grain of salt: (1) Coleridge (*Ancient Mariner*), (2) Pliny the Elder (*The History of the World*), or (3) Lot's wife (Bible)?

(c) Sow wild oats: (1) Samuel Bulter (*The Way of All Flesh*), (2) Shakespeare (*The Tempest*), or (3) William Blake (*Milton*)?

(d) Thorns of life: (1) Percy Bysshe Shelley, (2) Alfred, Lord Tennyson, or (3) John Keats?

(e) Tragic flaw: (1) Aristotle (in *Poetics*), (2) Shakespeare (in *King Lear*), (3) Virgil (in *Aeneid*)?

(f) Speak of the devil: (1) Milton (*Paradise Lost*), (2) Coleridge (*Biographica Literaria*), or (3) Shakespeare (*Macbeth*)?

(g) Point of no return: (1) an aeronautical warning used for a title by John P. Marquand, (2) Dante's fifth circle, (3) riverboat argot used by Mark Twain?

(h) Every dog has his day: (1) Shakespeare in *Hamlet*, (2) Aesop, or (3) Goethe, in *Dr. Faustus*?

(i) From the sublime to the ridiculous: (1) Thomas Jefferson, (2) Thomas Paine, or (3) Thomas Hardy?

(j) Sweetness and light: (1) Jonathan Swift (*Battle of the Books*), (2) Homer (*The Iliad*), or (3) Bunyan (*The Pilgrim's Progress*)?

41 Upton Sinclair titled his Pulitzer Prize-winning novel *Dragon's Teeth.* From what Roman philosopher did he take the image? (a) Ovid, the *Metamorphosis,* (b) Plato, *The Republic,* (c) Horace, *The Epistles*?

42 With the words, "look homeward, Angel," John Milton, in *Lycidas,* addresses a dead friend who has become an angel, asking him to look back with pity on mourners who have been left behind. What twentieth-century American author used that quotation for the title of his novel?

43 A common expression is "Hobson's choice." Who was the original Hobson, and what was his choice?

44 Dante's *Inferno* had nine circles that moved from the least punishing (the first circle) to the most severe (the ninth). What contemporary Russian writer alludes to Dante's formula in describing the penal system of the Soviet Union under Stalin.

45 Long before Margaret Mitchell used it as the title for her Civil War novel, an English poet, who died by drinking too much absinth and falling off his barstool, used the expression "gone with the wind" in his poem *Non*

Sum Qualis Eram Bonae Sub Regno Cynarae. Was the poet: (a) Ernest Dowson, (b) Algernon Charles Swinburne, or (c) Dante Gabriel Rossetti?

46 Can you match the familiar expressions to their sources?

Expression	Source
1. the child is father to the man	**(a)** Shelley, "To a Skylark"
2. blithe spirit	**(b)** Burns, "To a Louse"
3. all is vanity	**(c)** Bible, Ecclesiastes 1:2
4. hell hath no fury like a woman scorned	**(d)** Wordsworth, "My Heart Leaps Up."
5. no love lost	**(e)** Congreve, *The Mourning Bride.*
6. the law is an ass	**(f)** Cervantes, *Don Quixote*
7. method to his madness	**(g)** Robert Burton, *The Anatomy of Melancholy*
8. to see ourselves as others see us	**(h)** Shakespeare, *Othello*
9. penny wise, pound foolish	**(i)** *The Bhagavad Gita*
10. wear my heart upon my sleeve	**(j)** George B. Shaw, *Man and Superman*
11. I am become Death, the shatterer of worlds.	**(k)** Shakespeare, *Hamlet*
12. in cold blood	**(l)** Dickens, *Oliver Twist*

Answers

① *(b) "Leave her to heaven" were words spoken to Hamlet by the ghost of Hamlet's father, the dead king. The "her" refers to Queen Gertrude, Hamlet's mother, who married her brother-in-law, murderer of the king. The remark intends to warn Hamlet not to punish his mother, but to leave that to the judgment of God.*

② *(b) This comes from "The 23rd Psalm," known as "The Lord is My Shepherd," in which these lines occur: "He helps me to lie down in green pastures; He leads me beside the still waters . . ."*

③ *(a) John Bunyan. In his religious allegory* The Pilgrim's Progress *(1678), Bunyan wrote about a little town called Vanity in which tempting but corrupting wares and worldly pleasures were displayed for sale at a fair by devils and other questionable personages.*

④ *Ernest Hemingway appropriated the concept of the "haves" and "have nots" from Cervantes. He called it his worst novel, though it became a Howard Hawks film in which Lauren Bacall was introduced.*

⑤ *(b)* Horseman, Pass By *is a novel by Larry McMurtry. The horseman may also allude to one of the Four Horsemen of the Apocalypse in Revelations.*

⑥ *The book is* The Grapes of Wrath; *the author is John Steinbeck.*

⑦ *Metaphysical poet, John Donne, in a poem called "Death be Not Proud," speaks of death as being only a short sleep. Death, too, Donne says, will die, as the life cycle begins again for everyone; therefore, death conquers nothing and has no reason to be proud.*

⑧ *(c) William Golding wrote the novel of this name. "Lord of the Flies" is another name for Baalzebub, a devil or false god in Kings II:1 in the Bible. John Milton in* Paradise Lost, *mentions Beelzebub (another spelling), and John Bunyan equates Beelzebub with Satan in* The Pilgrim's Progress. *In Golding's work, evil, or original sin, haunts the young boys even outside civilization, suggesting that evil is present in nature itself.*

⑨ *(c) Mr. Kurtz appears in Conrad's* The Heart of Darkness. *He looks on the heart of man, in which he finds darkness, says "Oh, the horror! the horror!" and dies. Eliot describes the emptiness of mankind in his poem.*

⑩ *In his Ode: Intimations of Immortality, William Wordsworth uses the words "splendor in the grass . . . glory in the flower" to refer to the joy of being young, trusting, and possessed of a simple faith. William Inge wrote the screenplay for the 1961 film.*

⑪ *Hemingway borrowed it from Ecclesiastes 1:5, which refers to the futility of human struggle in the larger picture of nature. The sun rises, the wind blows, and man's effort is as nothing.*

⑫ *(a) John Milton wrote* Samson Agonistes, *or the agonies (struggles) of Samson. Milton, of course, took Samson from the Biblical account.*

⑬ *F. Scott Fitzgerald took the words from Keats for the title of his 1934 novel about a mentally ill woman and her physician husband.*

⑭ *(b) Will Faulkner stole this from Will Shakespeare who put these words in the mouth of Macbeth. Life, says Macbeth, "is a tale told by an idiot, full of sound and fury, signifying nothing."*

⑮ *The citation is "A Dream Deferred" (poem) "dries up like a raisin in the wind" (line).*

⑯ *(b) The stage directions that appear frequently are "Another part of the forest." (Shakespeare also wrote "Enter: Will Kemp" several times in the original folios, indicating when a certain actor of his time was to come onstage.)*

⑰ *(b)* The Bonfire of the Vanities *by Tom Wolfe. The "vanities" of Savonarola were the items he burned, which he considered cor-*

rupting and evil. Wolfe satirizes these vanities as he sees them in New York City in the twentieth century.

⑱ *(b) Yeats wrote these lines in "A Prayer for My Daughter."*

⑲ *(b) Aldous Huxley used it for his novel* Brave New World.

⑳ *(b) "No man is an island" is the first line of the work that contains the words Hemingway borrowed for his title. The poet is John Donne, although these lines come from one of his prose writings, "Devotions upon Emergent Occasions."*

㉑ *(b) Beulah land occurs in the Biblical Book of Isaiah to indicate a fruitful land of "corn and grapes" given to those in whom the Lord "delights."*

㉒ *(c) Electra was the daughter of King Agamemnon, whose death she revenged by helping her brother Orestes plan the murder of her mother, Clytemnestra, and her mother's lover.*

㉓ *Andrew Marvell in "To His Coy Mistress," which begins: "Had we but world enough, and time,/This coyness, lady, were no crime."*

㉔ *(b) William Faulkner borrowed the Biblical Absalom to build a new story around. Faulkner's is* Absalom, Absalom.

㉕ *(b) This line comes from the Book of Job (19:20), in which Job, beset by more ill luck and cruelty than a man can bear, is simply hanging on by "the skin of his teeth."*

㉖ *(b) Miller refers to the original fall, Adam and Eve's fall from innocence in the Garden of Eden.*

㉗ *(a)* Ship of Fools *is the novel; (b) Katherine Anne Porter reworked this story for her novel.*

㉘ The Rime of the Ancient Mariner. *The mariner blessed all God's creatures before Mr. Herriott got around to it.*

㉙ *(a) St. John the Divine sees a vision of the second coming in the Book of Revelation. Christ first appears as a lamb, then comes as a terrible figure on a steed with a fiery sword in his mouth. He is greeted by Satan, a dragon, and his minions. Christ kills the minions and flings Satan into hell for a thousand-year stay.*

㉚ *(b) In his poem "To His Coy Mistress," Andrew Marvell says: "The grave's a fine and private place/But none, I think, do there embrace."*

㉛ *A grail is a cup. The Holy Grail alludes to the cup of Joseph of Arimathea that, according to Biblical tradition, caught the blood of Christ as he was crucified.*

(32) *Horace.*

(33) *Wire, briar, limber, lock/Three geese in a flock,/One flew East, one flew West/One flew over the cuckoo's nest.*

(34) *Lewis Carroll's* Alice in Wonderland, *an underground fantasy world.*

(35) *Shakespeare puts these words into the mouth of Richard, Duke of York in* Richard III. *He celebrates the end of a long, dark political period and anticipates his brother's accession to the British throne.*

(36) *The Wife of Bath tells a tale about a knight who goes in search of the answer to this question. The answer, he concludes, is that what a woman likes best is "to have her own sweet way."*

(37) *Robert Browning wrote a poem called "Love Among the Ruins."*

(38) *(b) Revelations.*

(39) *(a) Alexander Pope.*

(40) *(a) (2) Spencer in* Principles of Biology. *(b) (2) Pliny the Edler in* The History of the World. *(c) (1) Butler in* The Way of All Flesh, *written in 1903. (d) (1) Shelley in* Ode to the West Wind. *(e) (1) the term came from Aristotle. (f) (2) Speak of the devil, and his horns will appear, Coleridge says (g) (2) It is the title of a 1949 novel by Marquand, which he tool from an aeronautical warning. (h) (1) Hamlet, Act*

V,.scene 1/ (i) (2) in Age of Reason. *(j) (1) these are the "two noblest things" says satirical Swift.*

(41) *(a) In Ovid's* Metamorphosis, *Cadmus, King of Thebes, slew a dragon and sowed its teeth as if they were seeds. Where the teeth fell, armed men sprang up and made war on each other. Sinclair uses this image as a symbol.*

(42) *Thomas Wolfe.*

(43) *In* The Spectator, *Richard Steele tells a story of a man named Hobson who leased horses, but customers must take the horse nearest the door or take none at all. Therefore, Hobson's choice is no choice at all.*

(44) *Alexander Solzhenitzyn in his novel* Gulag Archipellago. *In Solzhenitzyn's work, the placement and harshness of punishment of the prison camps move out from Moscow, or civilization, much in the way that Dante's circles of Hell move into the interior of the earth. Dante's lowest circle is the harshest; the camp in the farthest reaches is the worst.*

(45) *(a) Ernest Dowson (1867–1900), from his poem "Non Sum Qualis": "I have forgot much, Cynara! Gone with the wind,/ Flung roses, roses riotously with the throng,/Dancing, to put thy pale, lost lilies out of mind."*

(46) *1(d), 2(a), 3(c), 4(e), 5(f), 6(l), 7(k), 8(b), 9(g), 10(h), 11(i), 12(j).*

Cogito, Ergo Sum Nonfiction: From Philosophers to Pundits

The people in the questions that follow write in many modes, from political studies and philosophical theories that have rocked the world to slight essays that amuse, from newspaper columns that take less than a page to histories that run to several volumes. Some have written biographies, and some, autobiographies. Together, these writers represent different countries, different philosophies, and different points of view. Let's see how many of these authors you know, or can guess, from the clues supplied.

1 Who wrote that "the life which is unexamined is not worth living" in the ancient Greek text, *The Apologia*, written in a literary form called the *dialogue*?

❷ Charles Darwin, the nineteenth-century English naturalist, gave us his theory of evolution in two works. One was *The Origin of the Species*. What was the other?

❸ What English woman wrote *A Vindication of the Rights of Women* (1792), which presents the first fully elaborated argument for political, economic, and legal equality for women?

❹ This seventeenth-century mathematician, scientist, and religious thinker came to believe that reason alone could not satisfy, and that faith was necessary. In his *Pensees*, his reflections on religion, he wrote, "The heart has its reasons that the reason does not know." Is he (a) John Locke, (b) Thomas Hobbes, or (c) Blaise Pascal?

❺ The thinker referred to in the question above made a famous "wager." Can you paraphrase it?

❻ *The Summa Theologica* is the best-known work of the theologian who in it discusses five ways of attempting to prove that there is a God. Is this theologian (a) St. Thomas Aquinas, (b) St. Augustine, or (c) Spinoza?

7 This sixteenth-century German religious leader's Ninety-five Theses began the Reformation. Who is he?

8 For a two-parter: name (a) the Italian political philosopher of the Renaissance who wrote a book advising rulers to use any means, no matter how ruthless, to rid themselves of enemies and keep their subjects in line, and (b) the title of the book.

9 This Frenchman of the seventeenth century, whose chief work is *Traité des passion de l'âme* (1649), is probably best remembered for his statement, "Cogito, Ergo Sum." Who is he?

10 This seventeenth-century English philosopher, who wrote *Essay Concerning Human Understanding,* claimed that the mind is a *tabula rasa* (blank slate) upon which experience records impressions. Who is he?

11 What seventeenth-century English political philosopher wrote *Leviathan,* in which he states that without an all-powerful government to rule them, men's lives would be "poor, nasty, brutish, and short"? Was it (a) Emmanuel Kant, (b) Thomas Hobbes, or (c) Jean Jacques Rousseau?

12 This eighteenth-century French thinker's major work is *The Social Contract.* He held that humankind, in a state of

nature, was good. Social institutions, however, corrupted man. Can you name him?

13 Who is the author of *On Liberty*, which takes the position that the state may interfere with the freedom of the individual only to protect other individuals?

14 Who is the eighteenth-century German philosopher known for these three works: *The Critique of Pure Reason*, *Critique of Practical Reason*, and *Critique of Judgment*? Was it (a) Hegel, (b) Kant, or (c) Schopenhaur?

15 In what work did Karl Marx and Friedrich Engles put forth their ideas that political and social structures are determined by the economic conditions of people, and called for a classless society?

16 A nineteenth-century French author wrote an essay, "J'accuse," which criticized the French government. For a two-parter, (a) who was the author, and (b) what specific act was he criticizing?

17 What is the name of the publication by Benjamin Franklin that contains proverbs such as, "God helps them that help themselves"?

18 The author of *The Psychopathology of Everyday Life* and *Totem and Tabu* is called the father of psychoanalysis. Who is he?

19 *The Second Sex*, written in French and published in English in 1953, is a study of the biology, history, personality, cultural life, and destiny of women. Who is the author?

20 What New Englander who said, "most men lead lives of quiet desperation," went off by himself to build a cabin in the woods and live off the land?

21 Who wrote *The Two Cultures and the Scientific Revolution* (1959), which has become the definitive expression of the division between the sciences and the humanities?

22 An American left the organized church in 1830 and founded a national literature on the basis of his new religious philosophy called Transcendentalism. His famous writings include *Journals* and *Essays*. Some of the essays are "The Over-Soul," "Compensation," and "Self-Reliance." Who is he?

23 What twentieth-century work by a descendant of two American presidents deals with the author's miseducation by his family and schools, and his negative experiences in social institutions?

24 In the nineteenth-century a Frenchman came to America to observe the penal system, and wrote a book about what he found. Can you name this classic of political literature and its author?

25 Who is the author of the four-volume *Centennial History of the Civil War* that ends with *A Stillness at Appomattox*?

26 Name the influential work by Betty Friedan that is credited with creating a revolution in the way women think about their role in society.

27 Match the autobiographical works on the left to their subjects.

Biography	Subject
1. *Black Boy*	**(a)** Russell Baker
2. *His Eye Is on the Sparrow*	**(b)** Maxine Hong Kingston
3. *Growing Up*	**(c)** Margaret Mead
4. *Blackberry Winter*	**(d)** Richard Wright
5. *The Woman Warrior*	**(e)** Ethel Waters

28 Whose autobiography is titled *The Autobiography of Alice B. Toklas*?

29 What author lived for several weeks with poor Alabama sharecropper families to write an article that became the book *Let Us Now Praise Famous Men* (1941)?

30 Desperate for money, Washington Irving, who wrote *The Legend of Sleepy Hollow*, wrote a public relations biography for a rich American businessman called *Astoria, or Anecdotes of an Enterprise Beyond the Rocky Mountains.* Whose life does he glorify in this book?

31 What writer gained fame for his expose of the Nixon White House in *All the President's Men* (with Carl Bernstein) and again with his story of power and influence inside the Supreme Court (with Scott Armstrong) in *The Brethren*?

32 What historian chronicled President John F. Kennedy's tenure in the White House in *A Thousand Days*?

33 For this two-parter, (a) name the author who spent twelve years in Africa tracking down the history of his family and published it in 1974, and (b) name the book.

34 Who wrote *The Autobiography of Malcolm X*?

35 Name the political reporter who wrote detailed books about the campaigns of certain presidential candidates. He wrote four such books, one on the 1960 election, one on the 1964 election, one on the 1968 election, and one on the 1972 election.

36 Two of the most controversial books of the late 1980s were *The Closing of the American Mind* and *Cultural Literacy, What Every American Needs to Know*. Both were by professors, and both deplore, in different ways, the increasingly low levels of literacy and education among the American people. Can you name the author of each?

37 Who won the Pulitzer Prize for *Profiles in Courage*?

38 Author of an influential newspaper column, "Today and Tomorrow," this political news columnist wrote *Public Opinion* (1922) and *The Public Philosophy* (1955). Can you name him?

39 A bestseller in the 1970s was a study of coming social and political changes called *Future Shock*. Who is the author?

40 An American historian was commissioned by Jacqueline Kennedy to write a book about the assassination of President John F. Kennedy. After its completion, she tried to halt publication of the book. For a two parter: (a) what is the name of the book, and (b) who is the author?

41 Martin Luther King, Jr., considered himself foremost a minister. His most famous piece of writing was addressed to eight white Alabama clergymen who had condemned his civil-rights campaign as "unwise and untimely." By what name is Dr. King's message known?

42 A Briton who had begun his writing career as a correspondent in the Boer War wrote a six-volume history of World War II. The series begins with *The Gathering Storm* and

ends with *Triumph and Tragedy*. Who is the author?

43 In Alexandr Solzhenitzyn's *The Gulag Archipelago*, what does *gulag* mean?

44 What man, whose name has become a household word, published the first dictionary in America?

45 What American anthropologist wrote the still popular *Patterns of Culture*? Is it (a) Ruth Benedict or (b) Franz Boaz?

46 What American anthropologist wrote *Coming of Age in Samoa*?

47 In *All Creatures Great and Small*, a veterinarian from rural England reconciles his theoretical education with the lessons he has learned as a practical animal doctor. Who is he?

48 What are the names of the two eighteenth-century English writers who perfected the essay as a literary form in the journals *The Tatler* and *The Spectator*?

49 What Scottish writer is best known for his biography of Samuel Johnson?

50 Edward Gibbon is the author of a monumental work on history. Is it (a) *History of the English-Speaking Peoples*, (b) *The*

Proud Tower, or (c) *The History of the Decline and Fall of the Roman Empire*?

51 Name the book that Adolf Hitler wrote in 1923 while imprisoned for attempting to overthrow the German government. For extra credit, what does the name mean?

52 The story of the discovery of the structure of DNA was described by a Nobel laureate in *The Double Helix*. Was the author (a) James D. Watson, (b) Francis Crick, or (c) Albert Sabin?

53 Name the nineteenth-century Norwegian explorer and anthropologist who wrote a book describing his voyage on a primitive raft with five companions. For extra credit, name the book he wrote about this voyage.

54 Author of *The Mechanical Bride* and *The Gutenberg Galaxy*, this Canadian teacher and social philosopher gave us the concepts of hot and cool media.

55 In the early 1970s, Dee Brown described the white man's conquest of America from the point of view of the Indian. Can you name the book in which this occurred?

56 What is the name of the twentieth-century American cultural historian who wrote *Darwin, Marx and Wagner, The American University*, and *Teacher in America*?

57 What is another name for the Chinese *Book of Changes*?

58 Can you name the businessmen featured in the following two notable "autobiographies," written in the 1980s? (a) Written with Tony Schwartz, this book glorifies the financial victories of a real estate mogul and castigates his enemies. (b) Written with William Novak, this book chronicles the life and times of the businessman who resuscitated the dying Chrysler Corporation.

59 Beginning in 1968, a New York poet spent several years in Public School 61 teaching kids in grades three through six to appreciate the poems of Blake, Shakespeare, Whitman, and others. He then asked the students to write their own poetry. He published accounts in *Rose, Where Did You Get That Red*, and in *Wishes, Lies, and Dreams*. Who is this poet/ teacher?

60 This contemporary American humorist wrote a series of books on age: *When Did I Stop Being Twenty and Other Injustices*, *It's Hard to Be Hip Over Thirty and Other Tragedies of Married Life*, *How Did I Get to Be Forty and Other Atrocities*, and *Forever Fifty and Other Negotiations*. Can you name her?

Answers

① *This was written by Plato (427?–347? B.C.). In his dialogues, a form he used for many of his works, the characters discuss philosophical problems and often argue the opposing sides of an issue. Socrates appears as a dominant figure in all of the early dialogues.*

② The Descent of Man *(1871), supplemented and elaborated on Darwin's original work.*

③ *Mary Wollstonecraft (1759–1797). She was close to figures of the French Revolution. She died giving birth to another Mary who would become the wife of Percy Bysshe Shelley and an author herself.*

④ *(c) Blaise Pascal (1623–1662). He is not only responsible for Pascal's wager (see below), but also for Pascal's law, which has to do with the application of pressure on confined liquid (its practical application is seen in hydraulic machines).*

⑤ *Pascal's wager is this: He chose to believe in the existence of God, because if there is a God, eternal happiness will be the reward of the believer; if there is not a God, the believer has lost nothing.*

⑥ *(a) St. Thomas Aquinas (1225–1274). Aquinas, a priest, was one of the greatest Christian theologians and philosophers. During a time of great intellectual controversy caused by the recovery of Aristotle's works, Aquinas proposed that faith and reason can coexist.*

⑦ *Martin Luther (1485–1546), leader of the Protestant Reformation.*

⑧ *(a) Niccolò Machiavelli (1469–1527);* The Prince. *Perhaps the most famous line from* The Prince *is "the ends justify the means."*

⑨ *Rene Descartes (1596–1650), French philosopher and scientist. His famous quotation means, of course, "I think, therefore, I am."*

⑩ *John Locke (1632–1704). An ardent defender of freedom of thought and speech, Locke maintained that political sovereignty rests upon the consent of the governed. Some of his political ideas were adapted by the founding fathers of the United States, and his influence is apparent in the Declaration of Independence.*

⑪ *(b) Thomas Hobbes (1588–1679). His philosophy led to investigations by Locke, Spinoza, and Rousseau, who formulated their own radically different theories of the social contract.*

⑫ *Jean Jacques Rousseau (1712–1778), a moralist and political theorist who thought than man imposed his own law, according to reason, which was, by nature, good.*

⑬ *John Stuart Mill (1806–1873), who urged many reforms, including emancipation of women, development of labor unions, and proportional representation.*

⑭ *(b) Immanuel Kant (1724–1804), a German metaphysician, was one of the greatest figures in philosophy.*

⑮ *This theory was recorded in* The Communist Manifesto, *a pamphlet written on the eve of the German revolution of 1848. The two also collaborated on* Das Kapital.

⑯ *Émile Zola wrote the essay that influenced public opinion when a Jewish army officer, Alfred Dreyfus, was falsely convicted of betraying French military secrets and was sentenced to life imprisonment. Through the help of Zola's article, Dreyfus was eventually cleared of charges.*

⑰ Poor Richard's Almanac, *which Franklin wrote and published every year from 1733 to 1758.*

⑱ *Sigmund Freud (1856–1939). His theory of the unconscious has influenced anthropology, education, art, and literature.*

⑲ *Simone de Beauvoir, for many years, companion of Jean Paul Sarte. De Beauvoir wrote novels as well as another monumen-*

tal treatise, The Coming of Age *(tr. 1972), an exhaustive study of the aged in many societies.*

⑳ *Henry David Thoreau (1817–1862), the naturalist who wrote* Walden, *and the political thinker who wrote "Civil Disobedience."*

㉑ *C.P. Snow, a twentieth-century English baron, author and physicist, married to the novelist Pamela Hansford Johnson.*

㉒ *Ralph Waldo Emerson (1803–1882), influential religious philosopher, social critic and poet, and friend of Henry David Thoreau.*

㉓ The Education of Henry Adams. *This work, written in 1907, describes the rapid decline of Western culture after the twelfth century when the Virgin Mary (a unifying force) was superceded by the Industrial Dynamo (a force of scientific disintegration). Adams (1838–1918) was the grandson of John Quincy Adams (sixth president) and the great grandson of John Adams (second president).*

㉔ *Alexis de Tocqueville,* Democracy in America.

㉕ *Bruce Catton (1899–1978) wrote these books.*

㉖ The Feminine Mystique *(1963) was instrumental in creating the Women's Movement.*

㉗ *1(d)* Black Boy/*Richard Wright. 2(e)* His Eye Is on the Sparrow/*Ethel Waters. 3(a)* Growing Up/*Russell Baker. 4(c)* Blackberry Winter/*Margaret Mead. 5(b)* The Woman Warrior/*Maxine Hong Kingston.*

㉘ *This is the autobiography of Gertrude Stein whose lifelong companion was Alice B. Toklas.*

㉙ *James Agee. (1909–1955) Agee wrote the text and photographer Walker Evans provided the pictures for this study of Southern sharecroppers during the Great Depression.*

㉚ *John Jacob Astor.*

㉛ *Robert Woodward.*

㉜ *Arthur Schlesinger, Jr.*

㉝ *(a) The author is Alex Haley, and (b) his book is* Roots.

㉞ *Oddly enough, Alex Haley. At first, the two claimed the author was Malcolm X, with Alex Haley, but they soon dropped the pretense.*

㉟ *Theodore H. White is the journalist who wrote* The Making of the President, 1960, *and so on.*

㊱ *Allan Bloom wrote* The Closing of the American Mind *and E.D. Hirsch, Jr., wrote* Cultural Literacy.

(37) *John F. Kennedy. In 1954–55, Senator Kennedy filled a period of convalescence from back surgery by reading about outstanding American senators. The result was his book* Profiles in Courage, *a series of biographies of U.S. senators from 1803–1948 whom Kennedy found admirable.*

(38) *Walter Lipman (1889–1974), dean of journalistic pundits.*

(39) *Alvin Toffler, journalist turned "futurologist," wrote this book, which was on the bestseller list for seventy-eight weeks.*

(40) *(a)* The Death of a President, *and (b) William Manchester. After a long, drawn-out controversy, a settlement was reached, and the book was published. Manchester said only 1,600 words of his text were deleted to satisfy the Kennedy's, but not a single incident was omitted and none of the deletions was made on political grounds.*

(41) *"Letter from a Birmingham Jail," written in April 1963.*

(42) *Winston Churchill.*

(43) Gulag *is an acronym for the Russian words "Chief Administration of Collective Labor Camps." In Stalin's time, the gulags comprised Russia's penal system. Solzhenitzyn calls the network of prison sites across Russia, largely hidden from view, an "archipelago."*

(44) *Noah Webster, who published the first dictionary in 1828. (He had already published the first spelling book in the colonies in 1782.)*

(45) *(a) Ruth Benedict, student and, later, colleague of Franz Boaz, wrote* Patterns of Culture. *She did fieldwork among American Indians and Asian cultures.*

(46) *Margaret Mead, a student and collaborator of Ruth Benedict's, focused her interests on child rearing, adolescents, and culture. Among her works are* Sex and Temperament in Three Primitive Societies *(1935) and* Culture and Commitment *(1970).*

(47) *James Herriott.*

(48) *Joseph Addison (1672–1719) and Richard Steele (1672–1729). Together they formed the most celebrated British literary partnership.*

(49) *James Boswell (1740–1795). His work is* The Life of Samuel Johnson *(1791), which is considered one of the greatest of all biographies.*

(50) *(c) Gibbon (1737–1794) published this monumental six-volume work between 1776 and 1788. It is one of the most read historical works.*

(51) Mein Kampf *is Hitler's book. It means "my struggle."*

(52) *(a) James D. Watson. (Crick was his collaborator on the discovery of the double helix. Sabin perfected the oral polio vaccine.)*

(53) *Thor Heyerdahl. To support his thesis that the first settlers of Polynesia were of South American origin, Heyerdahl made the crossing from Peru to the Tuamotu Islands on a raft, which he called "Kon Tiki."* Kon Tiki *is the name of Heyerdahl's book about this sea-going adventure.*

(54) *Marshall McLuhan, influential social philosopher of the 1960s.*

(55) Bury My Heart at Wounded Knee.

(56) *Jaques Barzun, American cultural historian, social critic, editor, and teacher.*

(57) I Ching, *an ancient Chinese book of divination.*

(58) *(a) Donald Trump,* Trump *(1988) and (b) Lee Iacocca* Iacocca: An Autobiography *(1984).*

(59) *Kenneth Koch, avant garde poet and dramatist, and educator.*

(60) *Judith Viorst, who is also known for her wonderfully funny children's books.*